World Puzzle Book

Andrew Dalwood

THE GEOGRAPHICAL ASSOCIATION

Acknowledgement
The symbols used as part of puzzles 71-75 are reproduced with permission of Ordnance Survey®. These were copied from the Map Symbol Flashcards which show selected Ordnance Survey map symbols and descriptions from the Landranger® series (1:50 000 scale) mapping. Contact Ordnance Survey (Tel 0345 330011) for your nearest stockist. Ordnance Survey and Landranger are registered trade marks of Ordnance Survey, the National Mapping Agency of Great Britain.

ISBN 1 899085 38 6

First published as *Geography Word Puzzle Book* 1991
This version first published 1997
Impression number 10 9 8 7 6 5 4 3 2 1
Year 2000 1999 1998 1997

Published by the Geographical Association, Solly Street, Sheffield S1 4BF.
The Geographical Association is a registered charity: no. 313129.

The Publications Officer of the GA would be happy to hear from other potential authors who have ideas for geography books. You may contact the Officer via the GA at the address above. The views expressed in this publication are those of the author and do not necessarily represent those of the Geographical Association.

Puzzle illustrations by Paul Coles
Design and typesetting by Ledgard Jepson Ltd
Printed and bound in Hong Kong by Colorcraft Ltd

Contents

Mixed puzzles 2

Word searches 1

Mixed puzzles 3

Word searches 2

Mixed Puzzles 4

Answers

Introduction

These puzzles are set with two purposes in mind. All teachers know the despair of the last day of term with the worst possible form or set and the feeling that something ought to be done. Here are some suggestions, some puzzles which might prove useful to fill the gap.

There is a more serious purpose. Geography uses many technical terms and contains much jargon. Many students are unfamiliar with them and have little interest in spelling them correctly, even if they know the meaning. It might, therefore, be an interesting way of starting a topic with a Wordsearch (pages 40-48 and 54-59). This might add some fun (for most students will not regard it as work) while familiarising them with key words which could be used later; it might even stimulate interest in the meaning of some of the terms. The Networds (pages 5-16 and 23-32) can be used as revision exercises or even tests at the end of a topic, to find out how much has been absorbed.

Then there are other quizzes. Perhaps you suffer, as I do, from accusations from other departments that people do not know where places are. So here is a chance to let the students find out where many places are, perhaps in conjunction with atlas work or within a systematic course.

If you ask 'For what ages are the puzzles designed?' let me say that they have been tested with students from 11 to 18 years-old (yes, the sixth form enjoy them and profit from them as well!), but some of the atlas work can be used for upper primary or middle school.

It may be that for some of the Networds teachers will not want to use the clues provided, but would rather devise their own clues in view of what they have taught. Excellent! Please do so.

Above all, enjoy these puzzles. They are meant to be enjoyed. If you get as much fun out of doing them as I have out of making them, they will have been worth the effort.

Since the first edition of this book, the world has changed, new countries have appeared, names have been altered and, for teachers, the syllabus has been revised. This set of puzzles has tried to include as many of the changes as possible, but it may be that by the time you receive this book, more changes will have overtaken us.

Andrew Dalwood
St Mary's School, Cambridge

Q1 - Rivers (1)

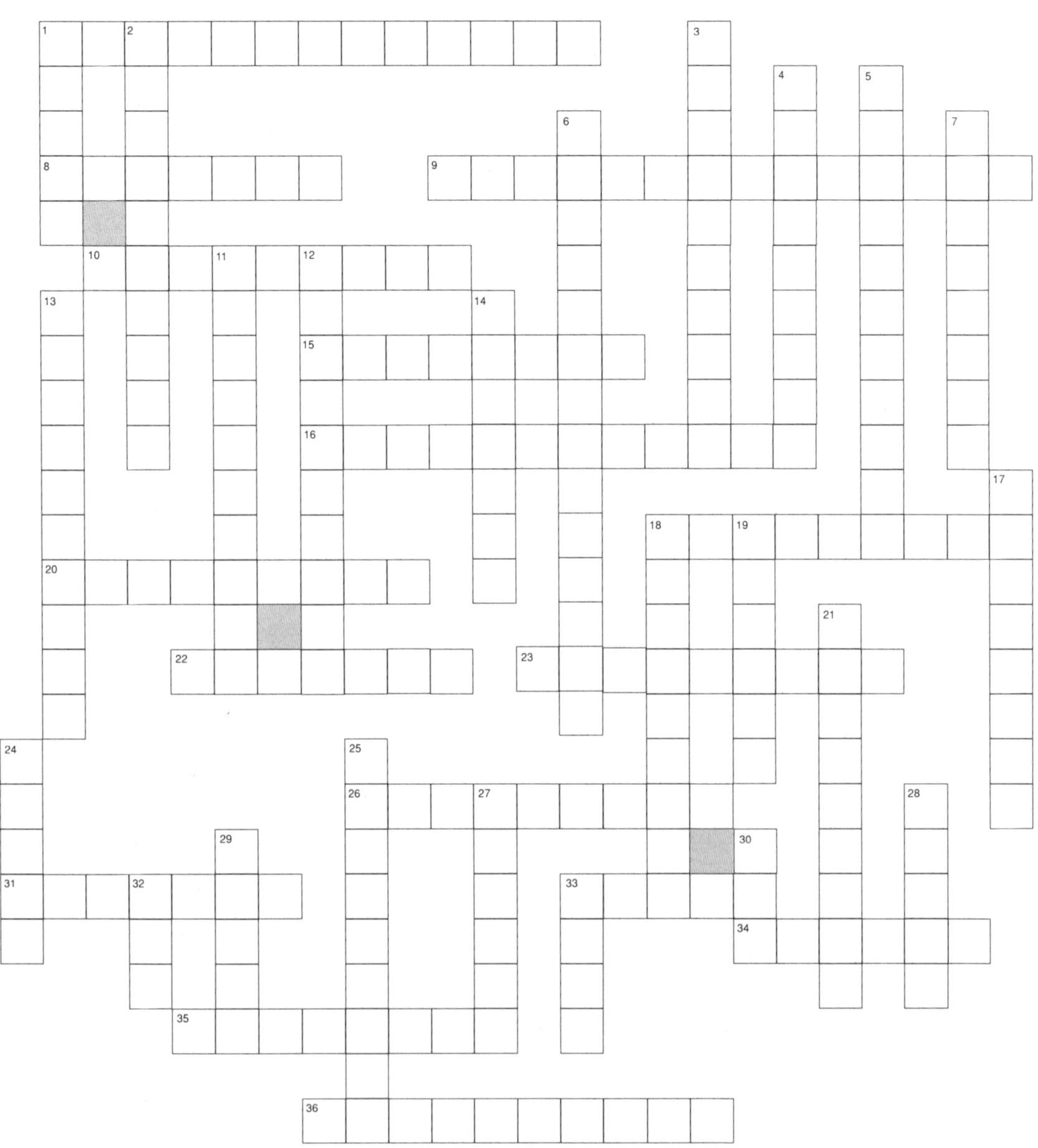

1 (across)	Total area feeding river (8,5)	19	Possible start for a river either in time or place
1 (down)	D-shape at river mouth	20	Building up
2	Drainage formed before present structure	21	Where one level meets another (4-5)
3	Cut-off meanders (2-3,5)	22	Wide loop of river
4	Divide between two of 1 across	23	Tree-like pattern
5	Middle part of a river (6,5)	24	Embankment along a riverside
6	22 cut into the land (7,7)	25	Vertical drop in river course
7	First stage of a river	26	Wearing away of load
8	Rectangular pattern of drainage	27	Where water crosses low resistant projections
9	Work of a river in carrying	28	Sharp bend at point of capture
10	Cutting down or down-cutting	29	Deep, steep-sided valley
11	Made young again	30	One shape of 1 down
12	Putting down by a river	31	Work of river in wearing away
13	Alternative name for 1 across (5,5)	32	Where most rivers end
14	River will do this to its bed	33 (across)	All rivers contain this
15	Swirling stones produce these	33 (down)	Sort of gap left at 28
16	Placed on top of the present landscape	34	Deep, steep-sided valley
17	Material dropped by rivers	35	Former floodplain remnants
18 (across)	Where all rivers try to get to (4,5)	36	Flat area with 22s across it (5-5)
18 (down)	One shape of 1 down (5-4)		

Q2 - Volcanoes

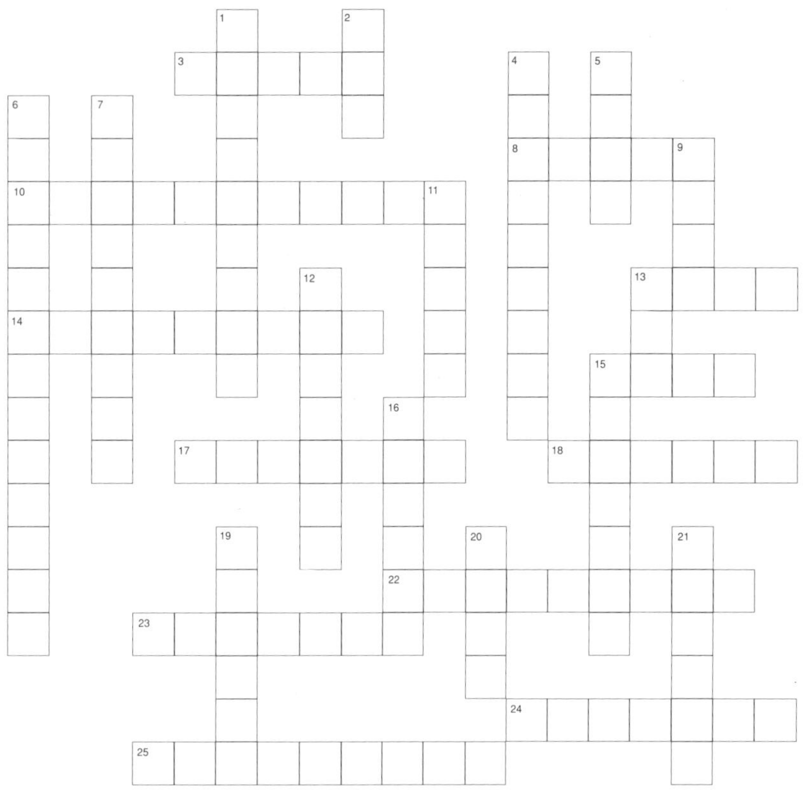

1	Domed intrusion
2	Fine material spewed out by volcanoes
3	Molten rocks extruded by volcanoes
4	Cone on the side of a main mountain
5	Hole at the top where the lava comes out
6	Volcanic landform made up of ash and lava (9,4)
7	Deep, massive intrusion, sometimes exposed by erosion
8	Usual shapes of volcanoes
9	Intrusion running along a bedding plane
10	Changed by heat and pressure
11	Some bombs have a bread- .... surface
12	Slowly-cooled crystalline intrusive rock
13 (across)	Exposed solid pipe of old volcano
13 (down)	French for 13 across
14	Vent where hot gases escape
15 (across)	Intrusion cutting across bedding planes
15 (down)	Sleeping volcano
16	Describes erupting volcano
17	Volcano which will not erupt again
18	Depression at the top of a volcano around 5
19	Very fluid lava, from, eg. Iceland
20	How lava moves when it leaves the volcano
21	Spasmodic hot water fountain
22	These may be shield shaped when made of 19
23	Long crack emitting lava
24	Broad basin from collapsed cone
25	Where water emerges from the ground at high temperature (3,6)

Q3 - Plate tectonics

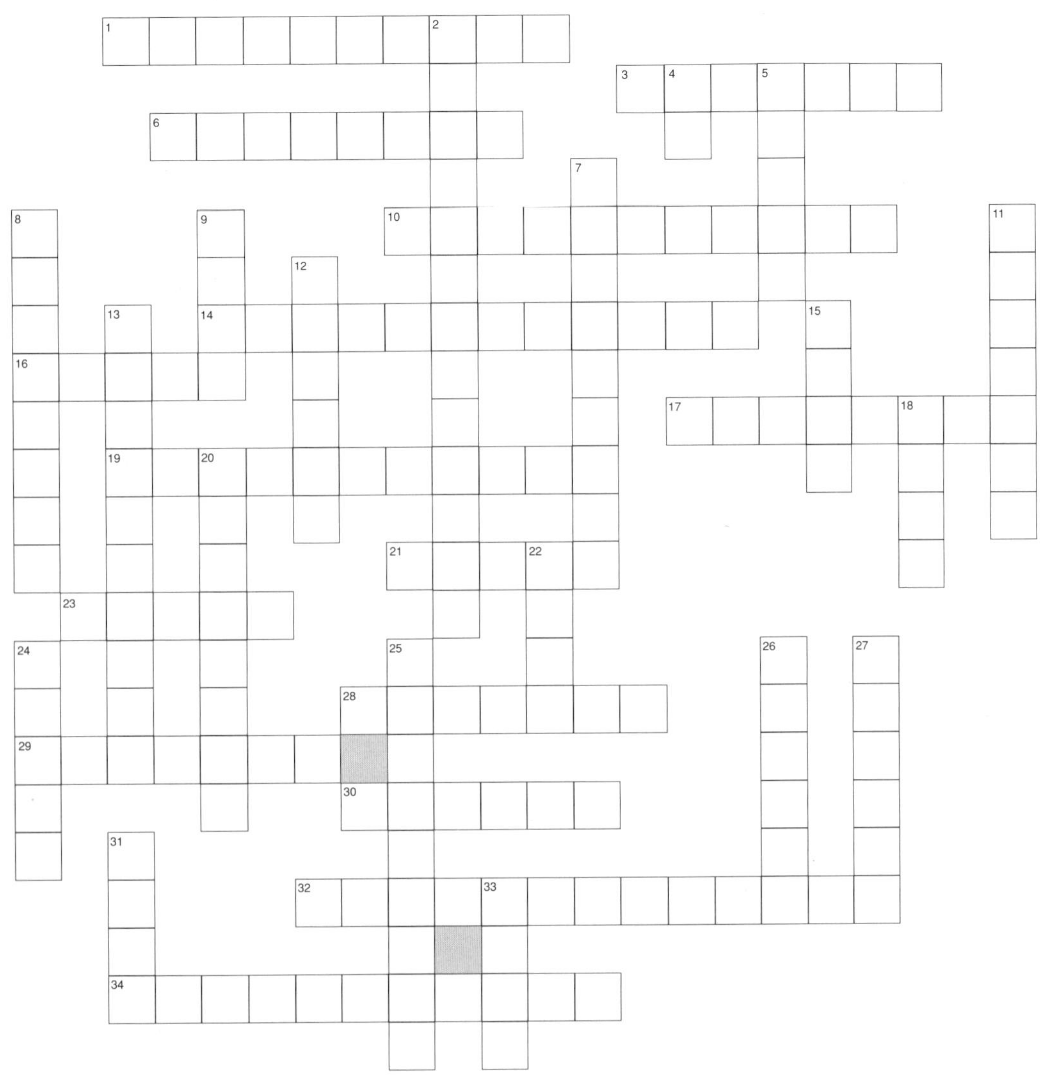

1 A shudder of the Earth's crust
2 The layer below the lithosphere
3 'All-Earth', the ancient super-continent
4 Very painful blocky lava on Hawaii
5 Flat-topped seamount
6 Type of lava from volcanoes in the Andes
7 Crust bit made mainly of granite
8 Ancient southern continent
9 A tear in the continent
10 Down this, earthquakes happen (7,4)
11 Where the molten magma reaches the surface
12 Deep-seated mass of 29
13 A 11 erupting under water produces this (6,4)
14 This is formed where two continents meet (4,8)
15 At the centre of the Earth
16 All continents do this, slowly
17 Ancient northern continent
18 Silica-aluminium (abbreviation)
19 The rocky layer of the Earth
20 To do with building
21 The surface layer of the Earth
22 Silica-magnesium (abbreviation)
23 One of a number which divides 21
24 Molten rock below the surface
25 Curved line of volcanoes projecting above the sea (6,3)
26 Ancient core of continents
27 The part of the Earth between 21 and 15
28 Japanese tidal wave
29 Makes up much of the continents
30 Makes up much of the ocean floor
31 Short for the boundary between crust and mantle
32 Where plates are being created (3-5, 5)
33 Shape of many volcanoes
34 Where plates are being destroyed (5,6)

Q4 - Clouds and rain (1)

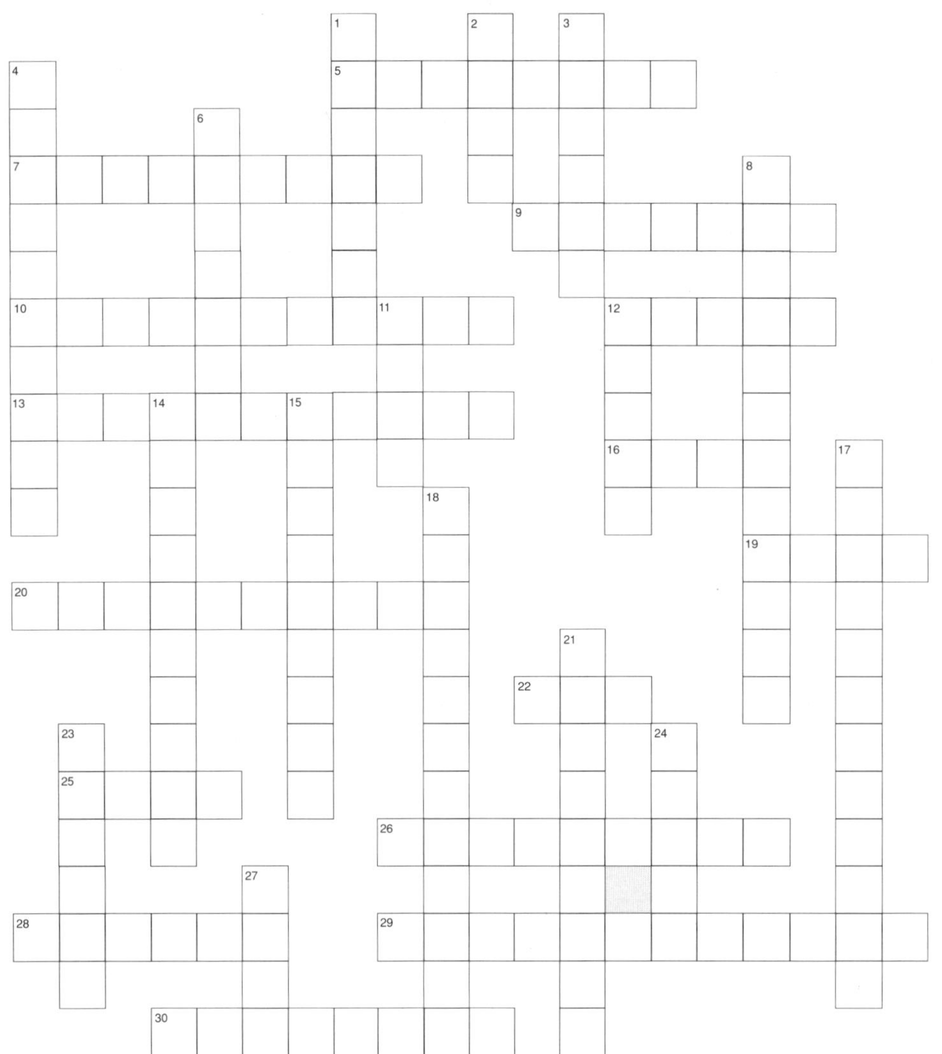

1	Loud noise from clouds
2	Visibility 1 to 2 km
3	Highest form of wispy cloud
4	Precipitation on going uphill (6,4)
5	Amount of water vapour in the atmosphere
6	Layer clouds
7	Bright flash from a storm
8	Sort of tower cloud that produces 1 and 7
9	Cauliflower clouds
10	Precipitation where two air masses meet (7,4)
11	Prefix for middle-height clouds
12 (across)	Mass of water droplets in the atmosphere
12 (down)	Prefix referring to highest clouds
14	Mid-level layer of clouds
15	Long word for type of rain in 4
15	Period of intense liquid precipitation (4,5)
16	The most common form of precipitation
17	Layer clouds at highest level
18	Vapour turning into liquid
19	Left her tail to form cirrus?
20	Large circular area formed by two types of air
21	Front edge of cold air (4,5)
22	Visibilty less than 1 km
23	Dry area in lee of hill is a rain - - - ?
24	Boundary between two different types of air
25	Frozen rain
26	Front edge of warm air (4,5)
27	Solid crystalline precipitation
28	Vertical pillar
29	Lowest, rainiest, layer cloud
30	Temperature at which air is saturated (3-5)

Q5 - Weather

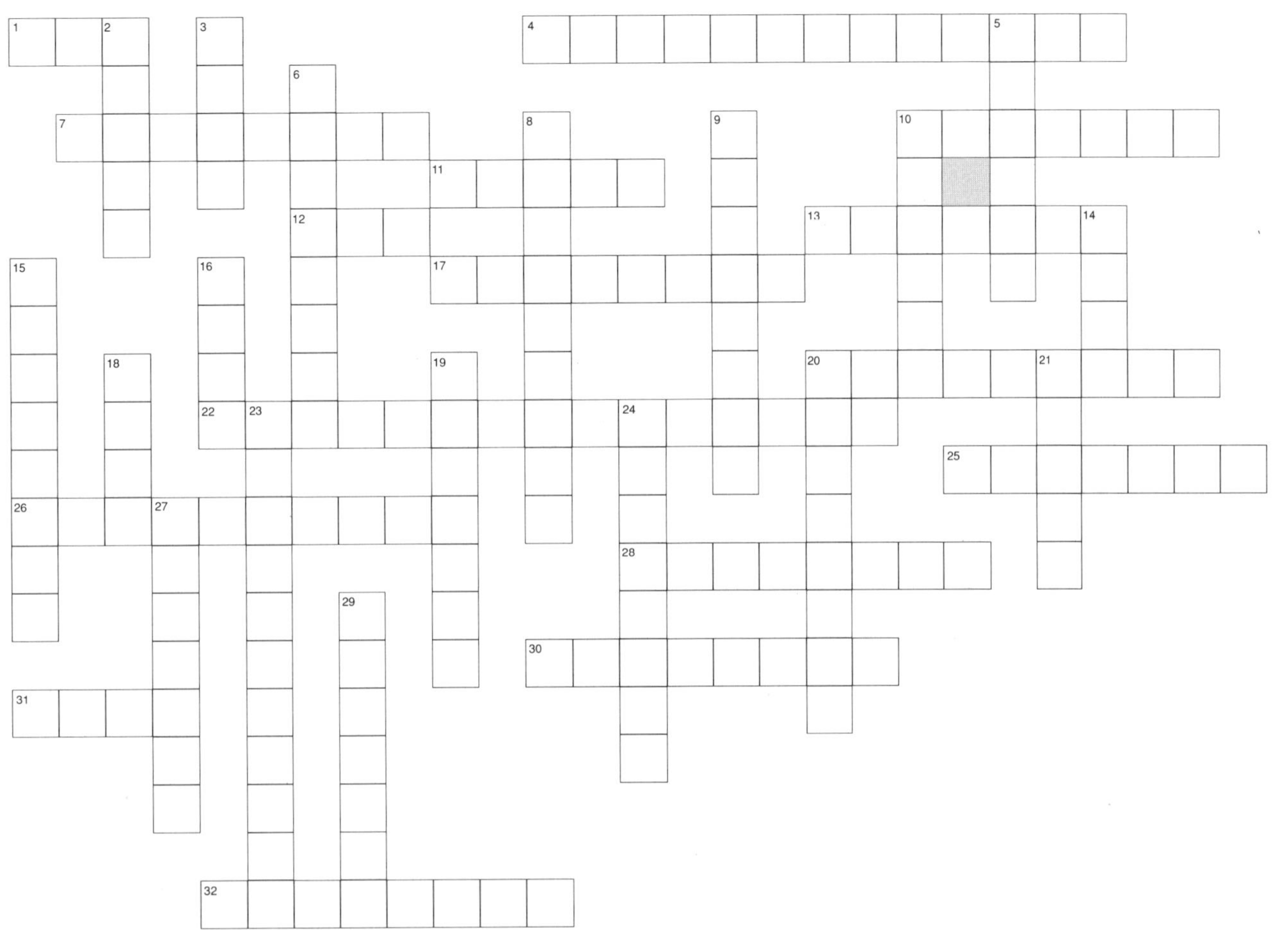

1	Visibility less than 1km	17	What the weatherman gives
2	Used for measuring	18	Water vapour frozen onto objects in the wind
3	Solid frozen rain	19	Form of 20 across without fluid
4	All forms of H_2O falling from the sky	20 (across)	Measures air pressure
5	Line of equal sunshine	20 (down)	Admiral of the wind
6	Shows the direction of wind (4,4)	21	Type of thermometer stuck in the ground
7	Amount of water vapour in the air	22	White box containing instruments (9,6)
8	Frozen dew (4,5)	23	Measured by 16 and 21 amongst others
9	Force exerted by atmosphere	24	Measured in hours; usually welcome
10 (across)	Line of equal rainfall	25	Found in some thermometers and some 20s (across)
10 (down)	Line of equal pressure	26	Measures windspeed
11	Dividing line between two types of air	27	The lowest temperature
12	Water that has condensed on grass	28	Form of 4, ten times deeper than rain
13	Line of equal cloudiness	29	Found in some thermometers
14	Recorded by thermometers	30	Intense snowstorm
15	Recorded by 2 and a form of 4	31	No wind
16	U-shaped thermometer	32	Temperatures are often reduced to this level (3,5)

Q6 - Coasts (1)

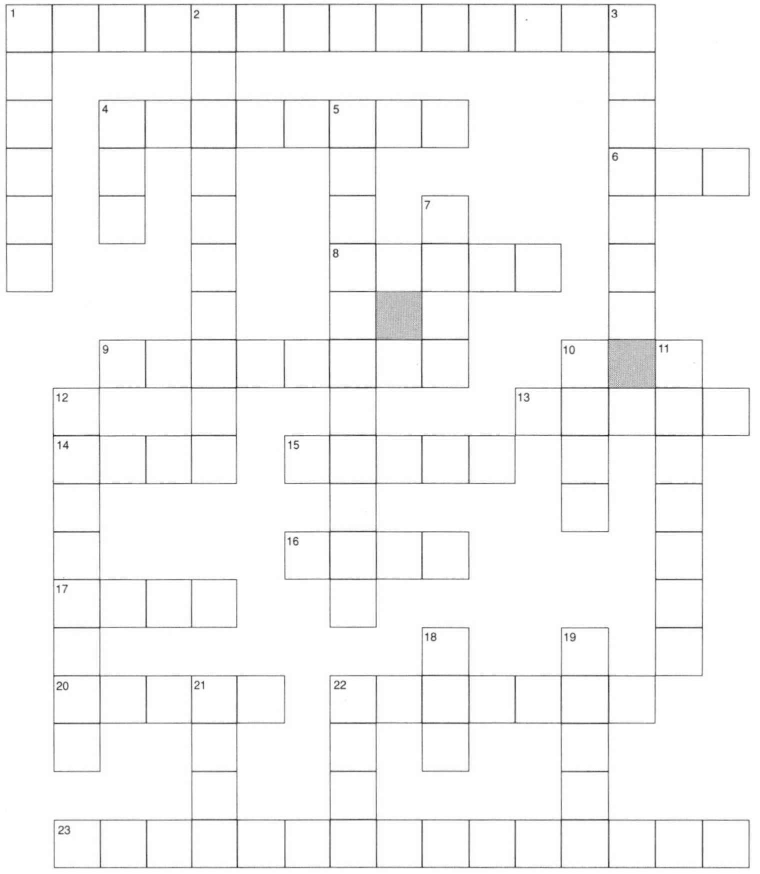

1 (across)	Movement of material along a coast (9,5)
1 (down)	Area of water enclosed by a spit
2	Very high pebble ridge created by storms (5,5)
3	Spit joining an island to the mainland
4 (across)	Result of partial collapse of cave roof
4 (down)	Spit right across a bay or estuary
5	As 4 but away from the shore (8,3)
6	Indent between two headlands
7	Sea with no waves
8	Waves running up a beach
9	Flat area of beach
10	Daily rise and fall of sea
11	Wave curling over
12	Water running down the beach
13	Drowned glacial valley
14	Where a cave has cut through a headland
15	Area between cliffs and low tide mark
16	Hole in cliffs
17	Undulation of the sea
18	Drowned river valley
19	Vertical part of the coast
20	Part of the headland left cut off
21	Nearly-circular indent in the coast
22 (across)	Pebbles on the beach
22 (down)	Sand or pebble ridge extending from the land across a bay, sometimes recurved
23	Flat area of rock between high and low tide levels cut by the sea (4-3,8)

Q7 - Glaciers

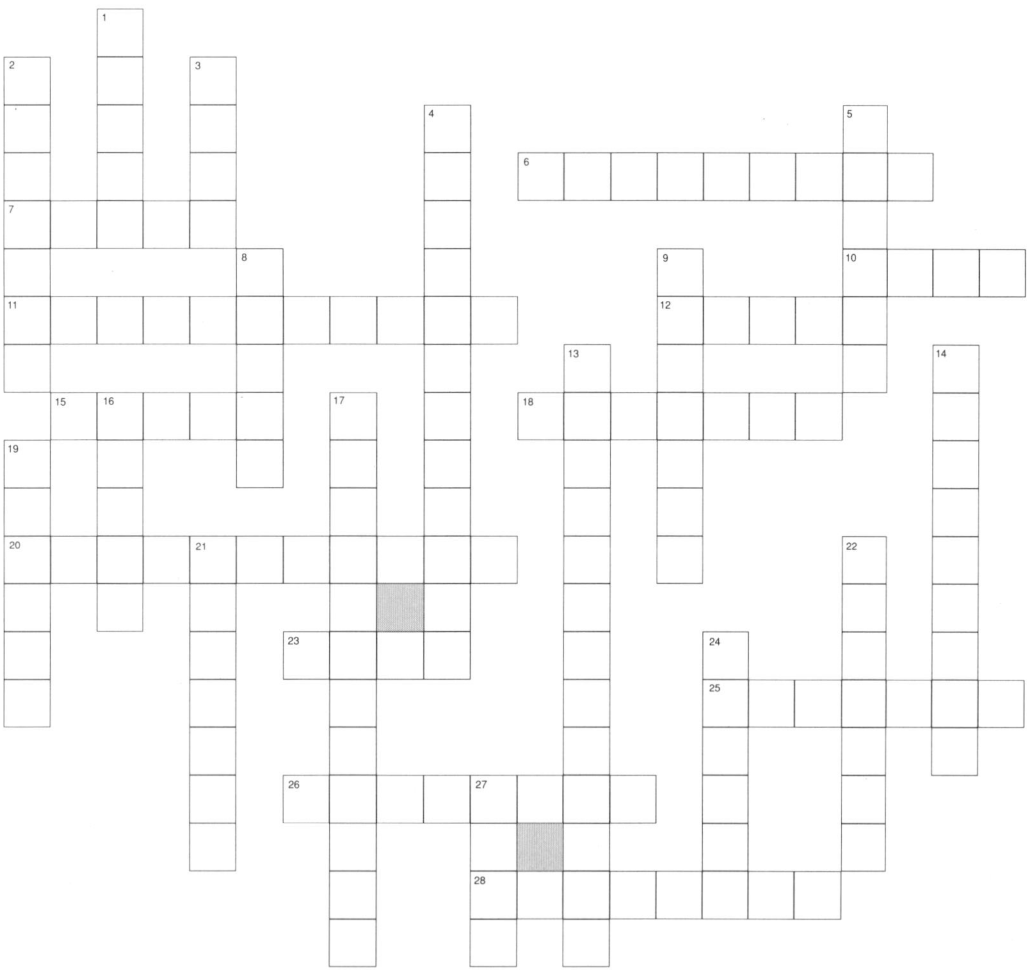

1	Weathered material collecting at the bottom of slopes
2	Isolated mountain sticking up through an ice sheet
3	Halfway between snow and ice
4	Beyond the edge of the glacier, covered with fluvioglacial deposits (7,5)
5	Glaciers follow and create this
6	Shape of a peak after creation of 24s
7	Ridge between two 24s
8	Drowned glacial valley
9 & 27	Hard lump with protected soft rock behind it (4,3,4)
10	See 19
11	Feature deposited by river in a 5 or 10 (8,3)
12 & 14	Ice-smoothed and plucked rock looking like a sheep (5,9)
13	Comes from a 24 and follows a 5 (6,7)
14	See 12
15	Sinuous ridge of material deposited by a sub-glacial stream
16	End of a glacier
17	Material dumped by a glacier or ice sheet (7,5)
18	A 5 created by a small glacier can be left like this
19 & 10	Long, narrow body of water in a glaciated valley (6,4)
20	Another name for 17 (7,4)
21	Egg-shaped mound of 20
22	Material in, on or under the glacier
23	Lake in a 24 when the ice has melted
24	French name for a bowl-shaped hollow where glacier starts
25	Periods with widespread glaciers (3,4)
26	Lumps of rock carried many miles from their origin and dumped
27	See 9
28	Mass of ice covering a very large area (3,5)

Q8 - Limestone (1)

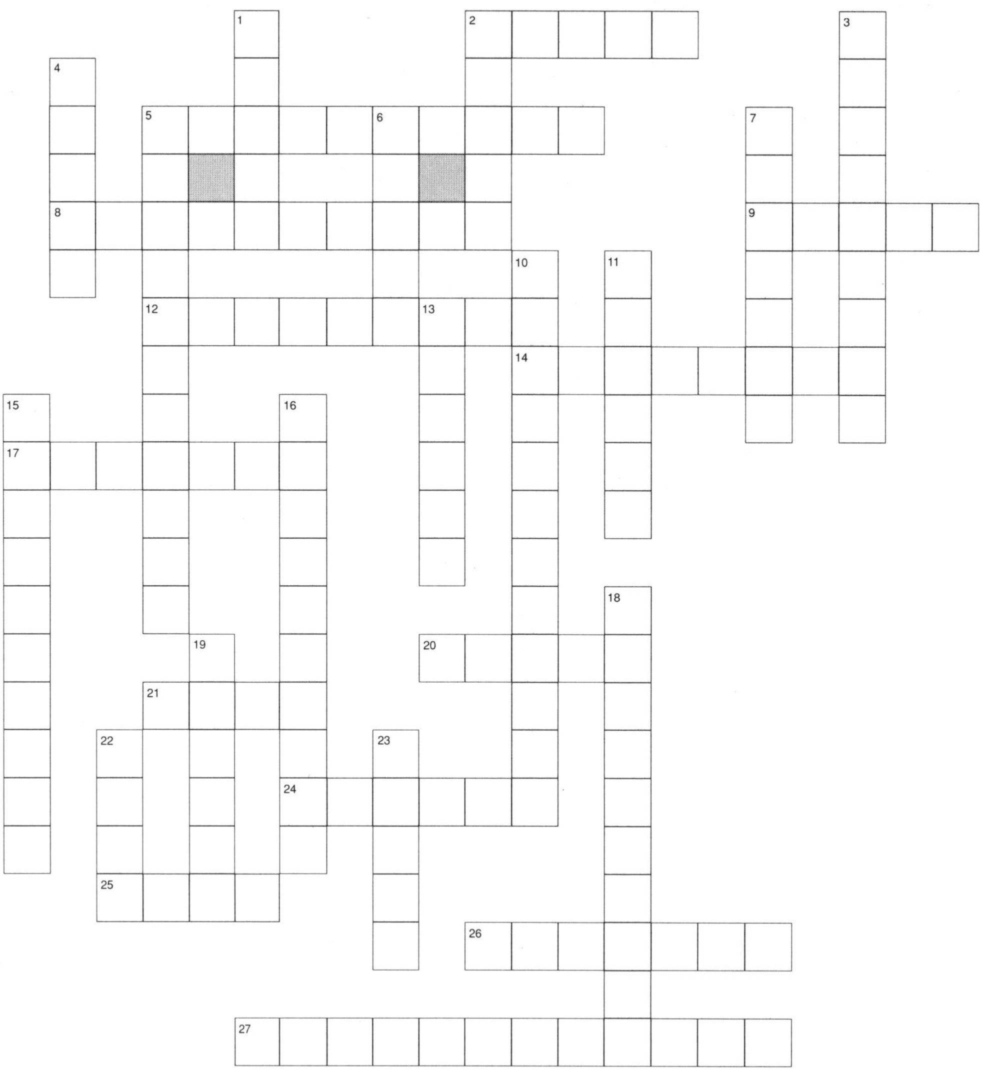

1	A large depression in a limestone area caused by the merging of several 11s
2 (across)	A deep, steep-sided valley
2 (down)	Deep groove in limestone pavement
3	Waterless stream course in a limestone area (3,6)
4	Area of former Yugoslavia with limestone features
5 (across)	'Icicle' of redeposited limestone
5 (down)	Hole down which a stream disappears (7,4)
6	Block on a limestone pavement
7	Hilly limestone area in tropical lands
8	Upward-pointing pillar of redeposited limestone
9	Soft, porous, fine-grained limestone in S.E. England
10	A surface separating layers of limestone - or other sedimentary rocks (7,5)
11	Circular depression on surface of a limestone area
12	Normal name of $CaCO_3$
13	Fish-egg grain-size limestone
14	Calcium-magnesium carbonate
15	Place where streams emerge from limestone (6-4)
16	Where a stream re-appears
17	Larger form of 5 down used by cavers
18	Red soil typical of Mediterranean limestone areas (5,5)
19	Large underground room
20	A very large depression with 18 on its floor
21	Tunnel in limestone
22	Small hills in the centre of 1
23	Vertical divide in limestone
24	Embayment in the scarp face of the chalk downs
25	Another name for 5 down
26	Limestone without many 23s or 10s
27	Rain is a dilute form of this and can therefore weather limestone (8,4)

Q9 - Rivers of the world

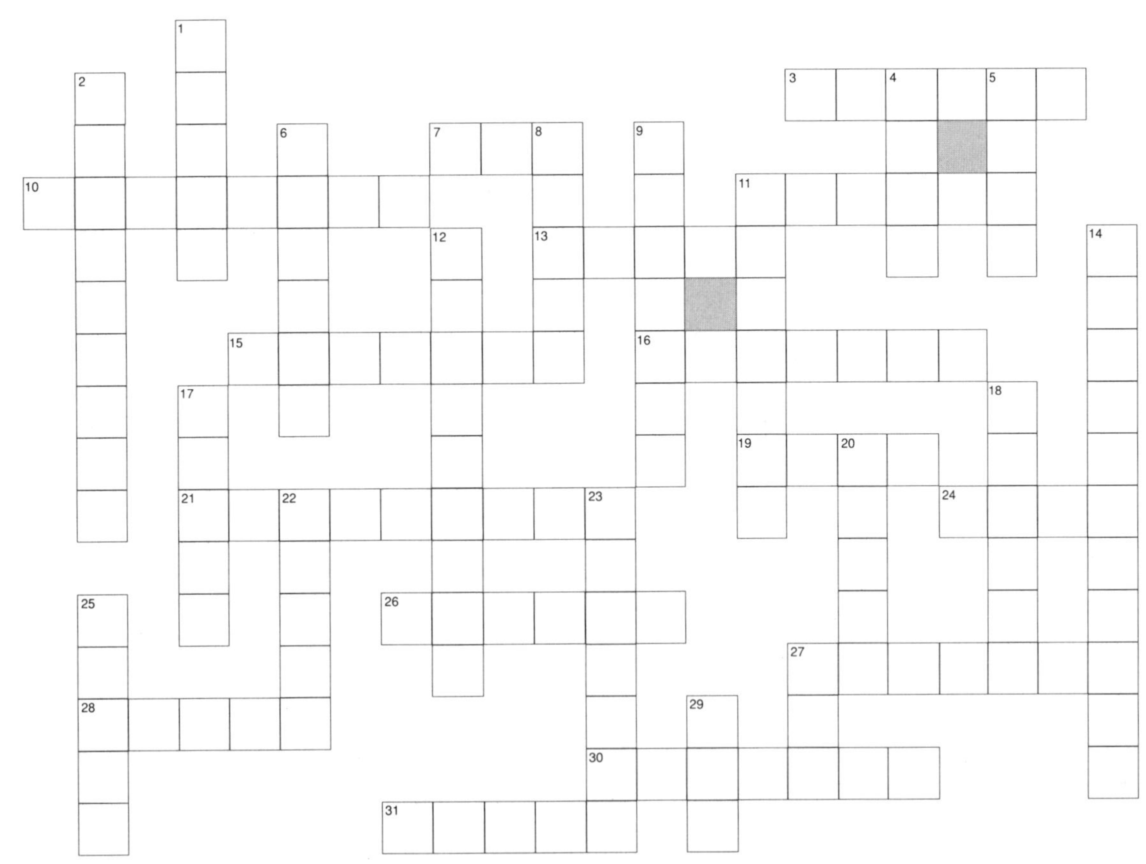

Name the rivers numbered on the map. The following are not on the map:

7	River of Innsbruck	27 across	River of Derby
25	River of Hameln (Hamelin)	27 down	River of Aberdeen
26	River of Phnom Penh	29	River of Emden

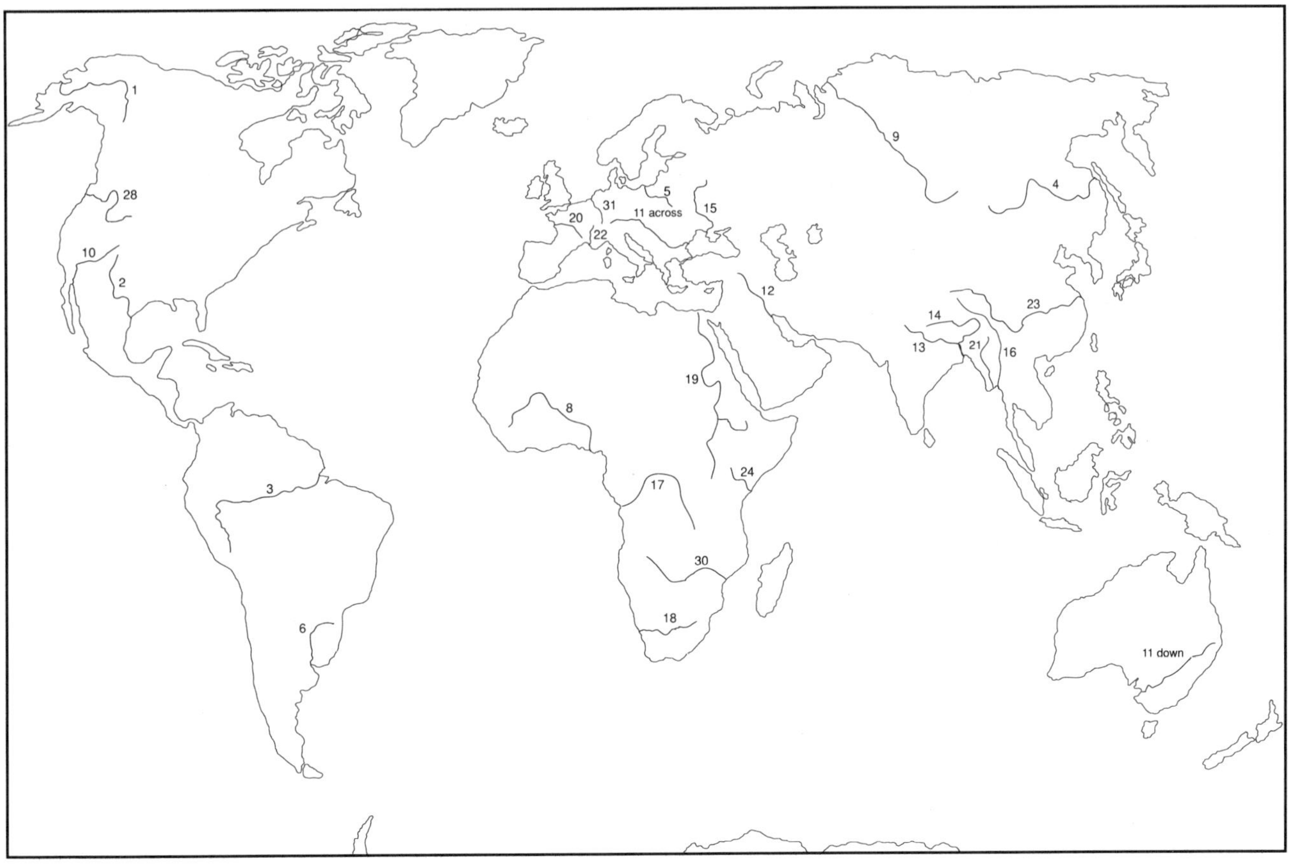

Q10 - Mountain ranges

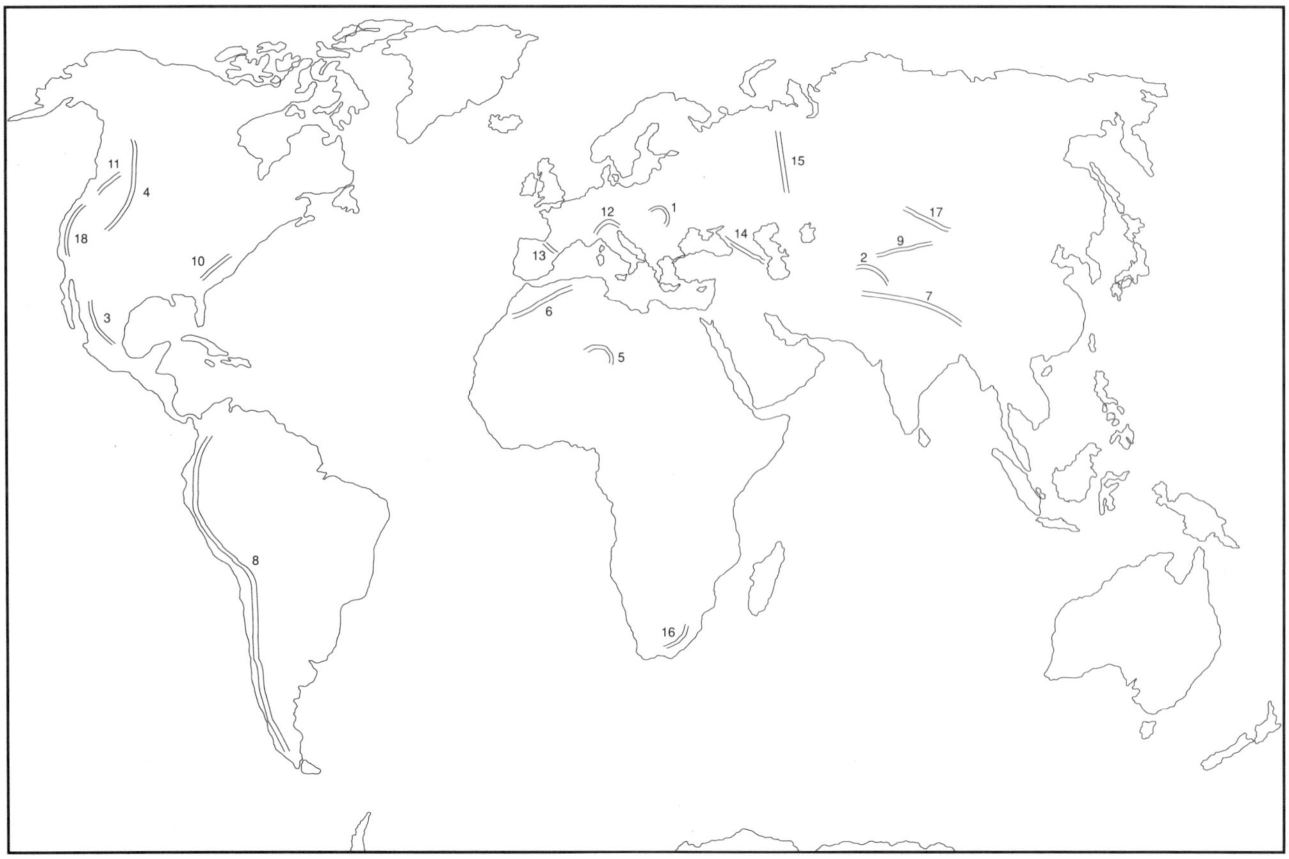

Q11 - Seas and oceans

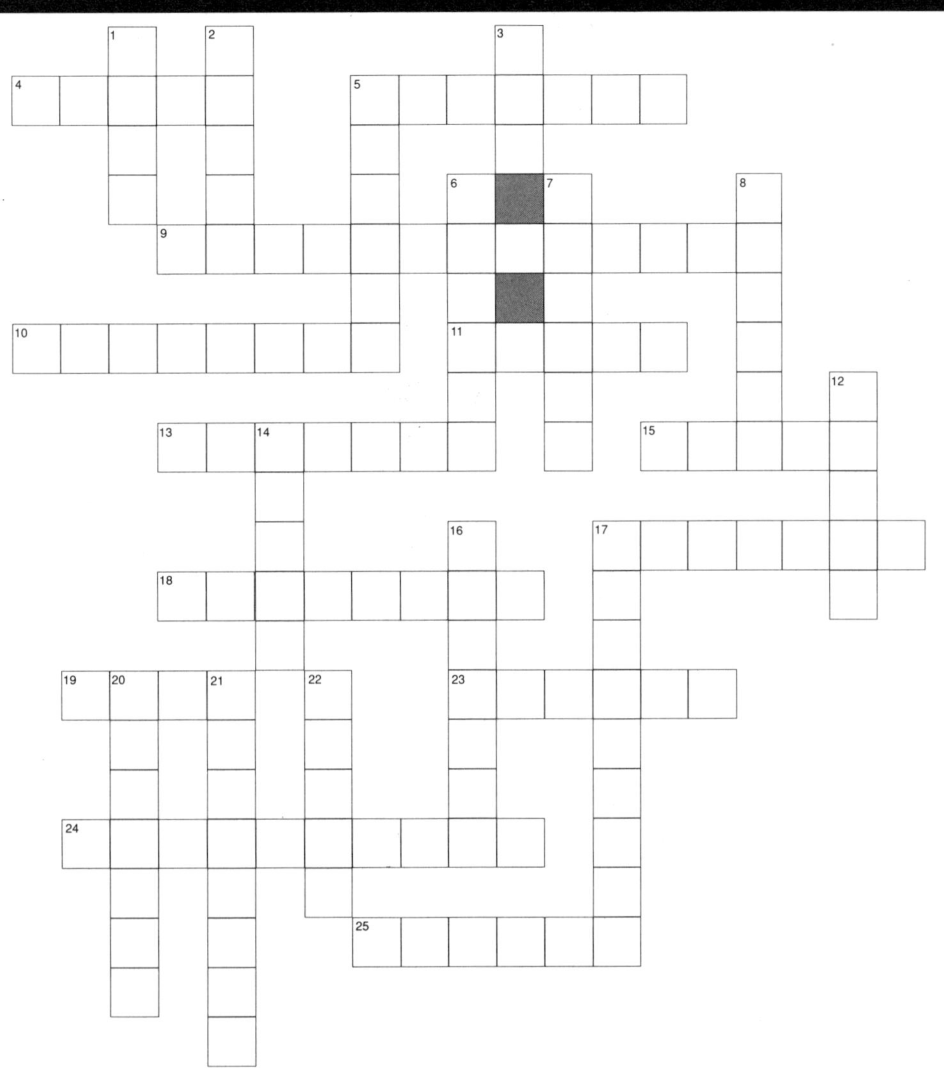

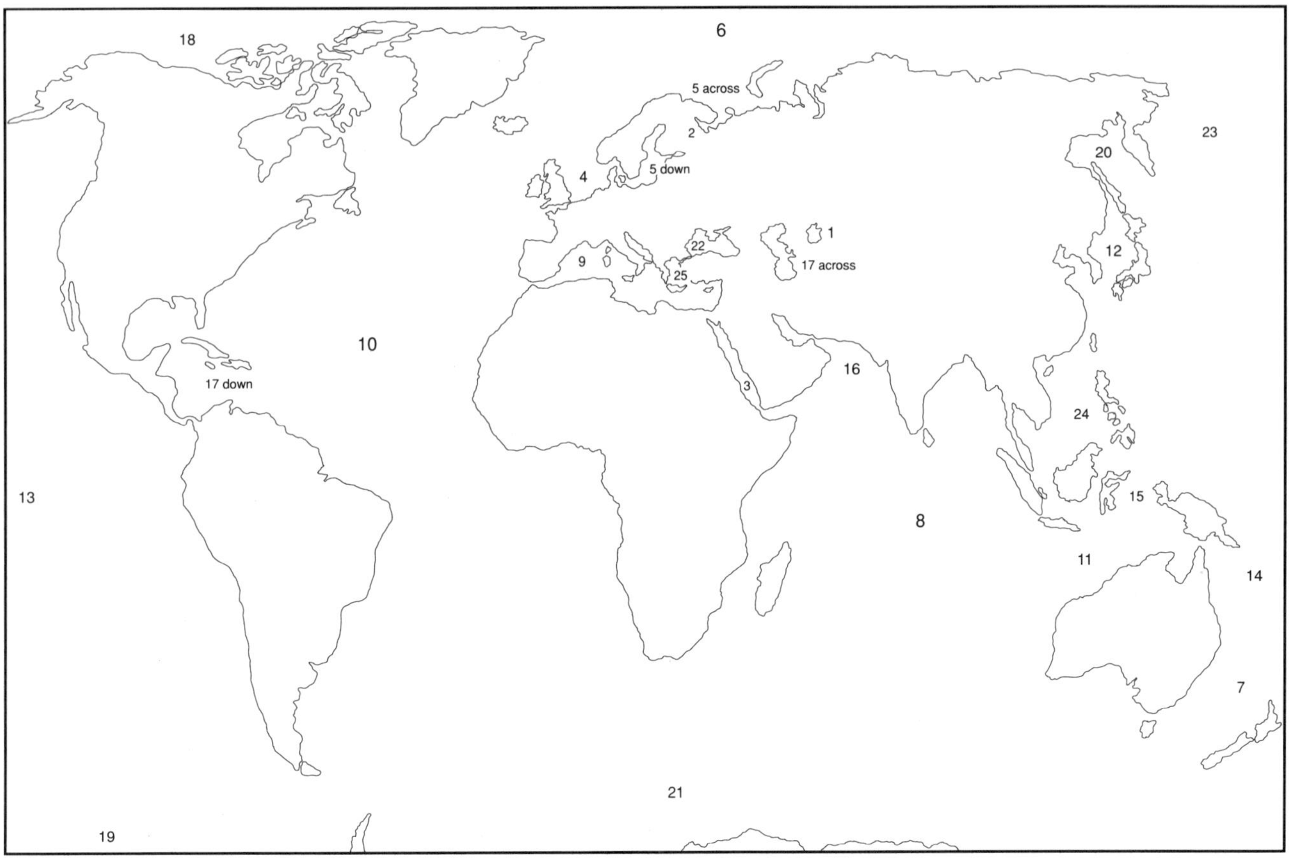

1
2
3
4
5
6
7
8
9
10
11
12
13
14
15
16
17
18
19
20
21
22
23
24
25

18
6
5 across
23
2
20
4
5 down
1
22
9
25
17 across
12
10
16
17 down
3
24
13
15
8
11
14
7
21
19

Q12 - Mines and mining

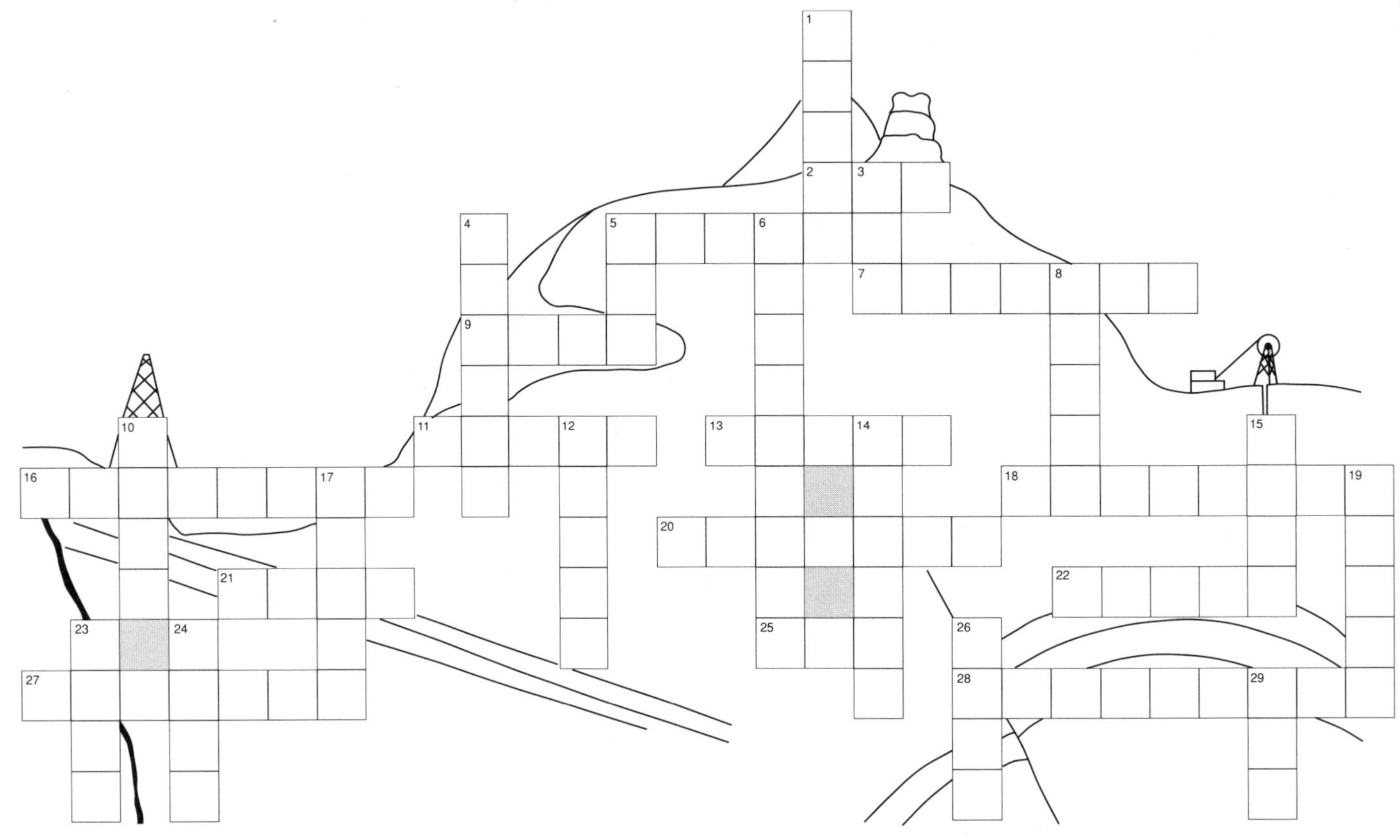

1	Bits of rock not wanted or needed
2	Outcrop of granite
3	Metal-bearing rock
4	Large hole in hillside from which rock is taken
5 (across)	Ores found in river-bed deposits
5 (down)	Hole in the ground or a coalmine
6	Hidden, e.g. under other layers of rock
7	Open, on the surface, not 6
8	Another name for 1 and what it does to the view
9	Shaft following a seam or vein into the hillside
10	Hole in the ground for water or oil
11	Another name for 9
12	An area of coal or oil or farmland
13	A (more or less) horizontal work area in a mine
14	Coal, oil and gas are used to produce this
15	Hole in the ground used to get coal

16	Extracting coal on the surface
17	Vertical passage to reach 13s in a 15
18	To do with river deposits
19	A bed, stratum or ________ of rock
20	Horizontal workface in a mine
21	A layer of coal in the ground
22	Rock that gives oil in Alberta
23	Narrow band of metal ore
24	Large mass of ore
25	You need to do this to get minerals out
26	Where oil is held in the rocks
27	A large amount or body of ore
28	A large area or amount of oil or gas
29	Liquid hydrocarbon, crude or refined

Q13 - Identify these rivers

1 Flows through Oxford, this river is twice ______________________

2 Sounds like six more than the one it is ______________________

3 "O ________ , Father ________ , to whom the Romans pray"

4 "The river _______ , deep and wide, washes its (Hamelin's) walls on the southern side"

5 Blue and waltzing along ____________________

6 "Way down upon the __________ River"

7 Is this river a type of net? ____________________

8 "Old Father __________ keeps rolling along"

9 River of the chateaux ____________________

10 Cleopatra barged down it ____________________

11 The Mother of India ____________________

12 Has Wagnerian maidens living in it ____________

13 "And quiet flows the ____________________"

14 Flows out of a garden and through Carlisle ____________________

15 2 Samuel 8 verse 3 ____________________

16 Luke 3 verse 3 ____________________

17 Battle, July 1916 ____________________

18 A citrus fruit in South Africa ________________

19 Named after a race of fierce warrior women __________________

20 A fat, lazy Womble ____________________

21 Fourth letter of the alphabet ________________

22 Boatmen sing on this river ________________

23 Dammed at Kariba ____________________

24 Great grey greasy river where the elephant got its trunk __________

25 One eye, one arm, one river in Canada ____________________

Q14 - Words in words

The answer is a country's name. In each case it is made up of the letters you are given and the word for which a clue is given.

1	_ _ _ LAND	Part of a fish
2	_ _ _ _ _ N	A root vegetable
3	B _ _ _ _ _ _	A girl's name
4	S _ _ _ _	An uncomfortable feeling
5	O _ _ _	A male person
6	R U _ _ _ _ _	Obsession or type of madness
7	_ _ _ A I C A	Comes in pots to spread on bread
8	_ _ _ L A N D	Frozen water
9	_ _ _ _ U G A L	Where ships unload
10	K U _ _ _ _	To stay for someone or something
11	D E N _ _ _ _	To give a score to
12	_ _ _ L A N D	Anger
13	_ _ _ A M A	Utensil for cooking in
14	_ _ _ G A	2240 lb
15	_ _ _ _ A P O R E	To use the voice in music
16	G I B R _ _ _ _ _	Large table at the front of churches
17	P A _ _ _ U A Y	Scrap of cloth
18	T _ _ _ _ A N D	Solid ice lumps from clouds
19	L E _ _ _ O N	To forbid
20	B A _ _ _ A S	Meat from pig

Q15 - Asian countries (1)

The answers are the names of Asian countries.
All you have to do is fill in the missing letters.

1. _ O R E _
2. _ H A I L _ _ _
3. _ _ _ G L A D _ _ _
4. _ _ L A Y _ _ _
5. _ _ D O N _ _ _ _
6. _ _ E T N A _
7. _ _ _ L I P _ _ _ _ _
8. _ _ P A L
9. _ _ I N _
10. _ _ _ B O D _ _

Q16 - States of the USA (1)

The answers to this are all states in the United States of America.
All you have to do is fill in the missing letters.

1. _ _ S H I N _ _ _ _
2. _ _ _ S O U R _
3. _ _ _ _ S Y L V A N _ _
4. _ _ _ G I N _ _
5. _ _ _ R I D _
6. _ L A B _ _ _
7. _ _ _ T U C K _
8. _ _ _ _ A S K _
9. _ I N N _ _ _ _ _
10. _ _ _ T A N _
11. _ _ E G O _
12. _ _ _ _ F O R _ _ _
13. _ _ A S K _
14. _ _ _ _ _ _ S I P _ _
15. _ _ _ _ A M P S _ _ _ _

Q17 - Europe

Fill in the gaps.

In Western Europe lies France, with three coasts, on the ________ ________ in the north, on the ______________ Ocean on the west and on the _________________ in the south. Bordering France to the south-west is the Iberian Peninsula, containing the two countries of ________ and _____________. Between the larger of these two and France are the _____________ mountains. To the south-east of France is the long peninsula of Italy, whose northern border lies in the ______. Along the length of Italy run the _______________ mountains. In the north of the country is the valley of the large river ____. The two large islands of __________ and ____________ belong to Italy, while the smaller island, _________ belongs to France.

To the north of Italy are the two small mountainous countries of ________ and _________________. North of these lies _________, once divided into East and West, which has the river _________ for part of its border with France. This river flows out to the North Sea through the small low-lying country of The ______________.

North of Germany is another peninsula which, with a number of islands, makes up the country of _________. This is separated by two narrow stretches of water, __________ and _________, from Scandinavia, which is made up of three countries: __________, ____________ and ___________. The western country, ___________, has a very irregular coastline, while the other two are separated by the _________ Sea and Gulf of ___________.

The other countries between Germany and The Russian Federation are called Eastern Europe, except the most southerly, ________. Five of these countries have the river _________ flowing through them or along their borders.

Q18 - Asia

Fill in the gaps.

The largest country in Asia, ____________, lies from east to west across the north of the continent. The northern coast lies on the __________ Ocean, into which run many large rivers, including the ________, ________ and __________. South and east of this country lies the second largest country, _________, and between them is the land-locked country of _________________.

In south-east Asia lie a group of six countries __________, ___________, __________, ___________, ____________ and ____________ through which run several large rivers including _____________ and __________. South of these countries lie hundreds of islands, making up the country of ____________________.

India occupies a large part of southern Asia. Along its northern border are two small states of _________ and __________ in the ________________ Mountains. India surrounds the country of _____________ in the east, through which the large river _________________ enters the sea. To the west of India is ______________ with another large river, the _________________, while to the south of India is the island of ________________.

Saudi Arabia is usually included in Asia. It is separated from Africa by the _______ Sea. Across The Gulf to the north is ____________ which has its northern coast on the ____________ Sea, the world's largest lake.

Q19 - Africa

Fill in the gaps.

There is a large number of countries in Africa and they are of different sizes. The continent itself has the ____________ Ocean to the west and the ________________ Ocean to the east. Off the eastern coast lies the large island of _______________ and several smaller islands. In East Africa lie the long thin lakes including _____________ and _____________ and the large circular lake of ______________. From these the river ______________ flows northwards, entering the ________________ Sea through the country of ___________. Between this country and Saudi Arabia to the east is the __________ Sea. On this sea, Africa's largest country, _____________, has a short coastline.

Most countries to the west of this have very few towns and straight borders. They are mostly in the _____________ Desert. In the south of this area is the second major river of Africa, the ___________, flowing into the sea in the Bight of Benin, through the country of ________________. The third major river is the Zaire which flows mainly through the country of ____________.

The country in Africa which reaches furthest east is _____________ ; the most southerly point is in _________ _________ ; the most northerly country is ________________ and the furthest west is Cap Vert in ________________.

Q20 - Scottish regions and Welsh counties

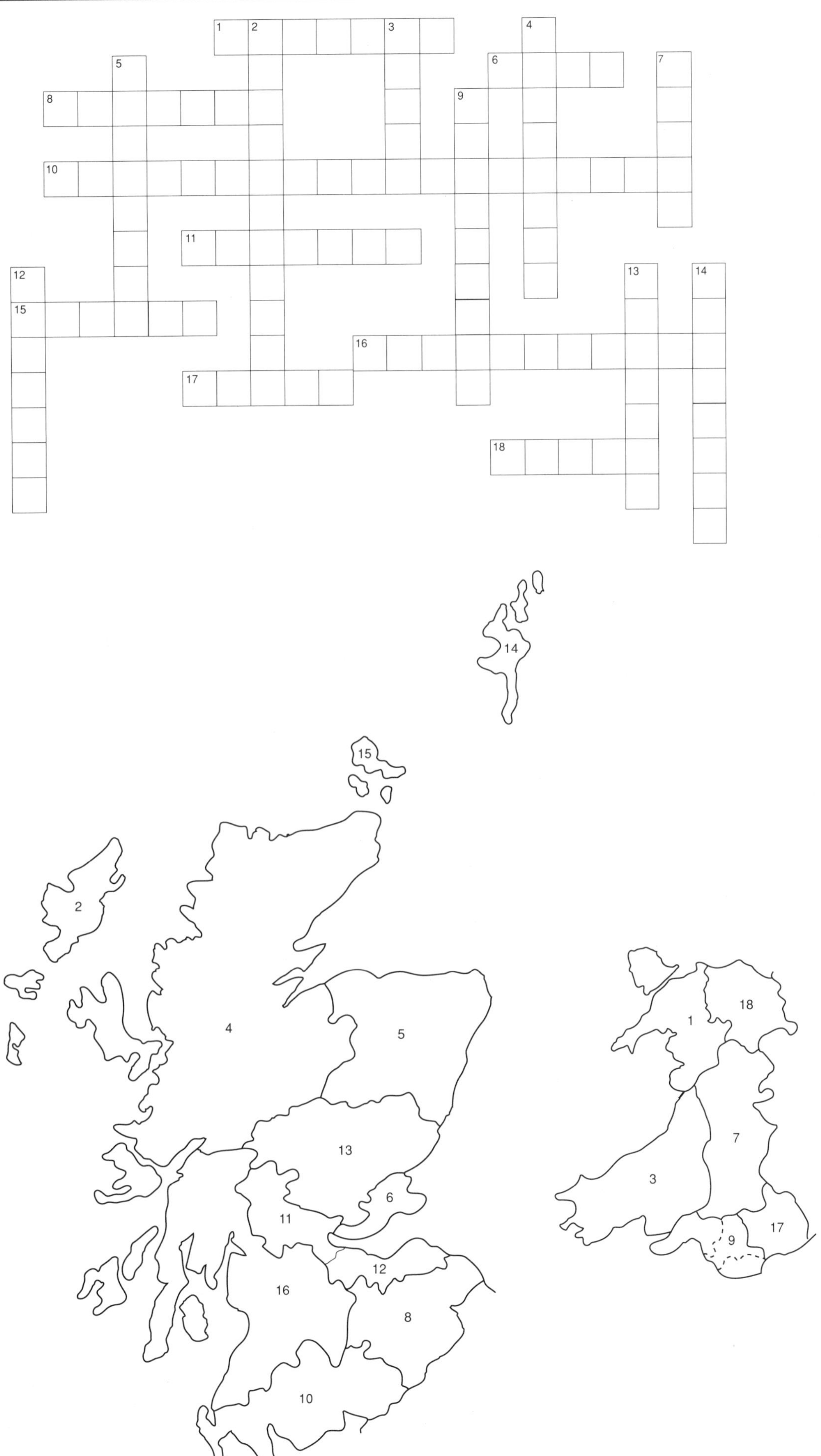

Q21 - African countries

Q22 - Asian countries (2) 1995

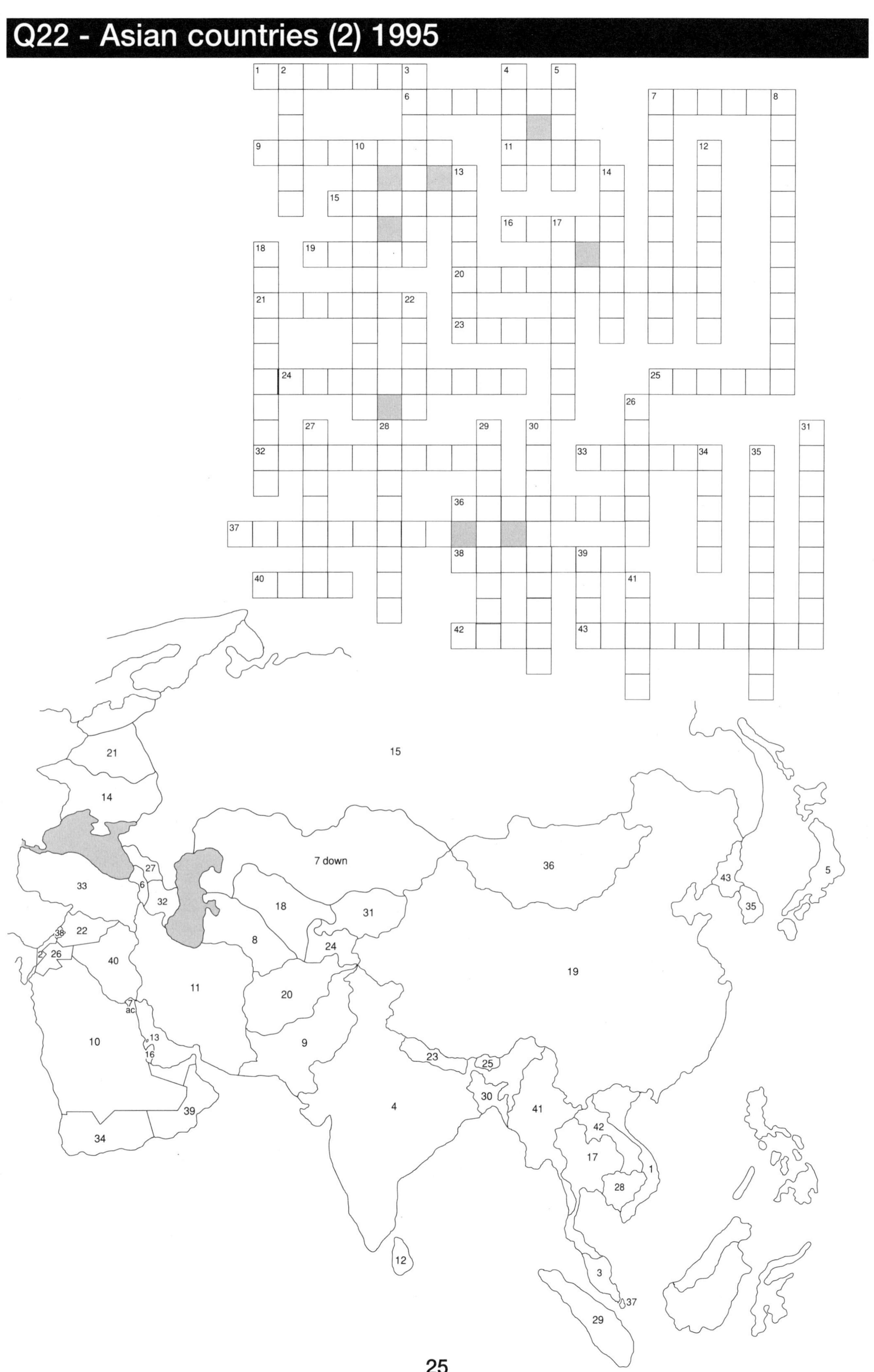

Q23 - European countries (1) 1995

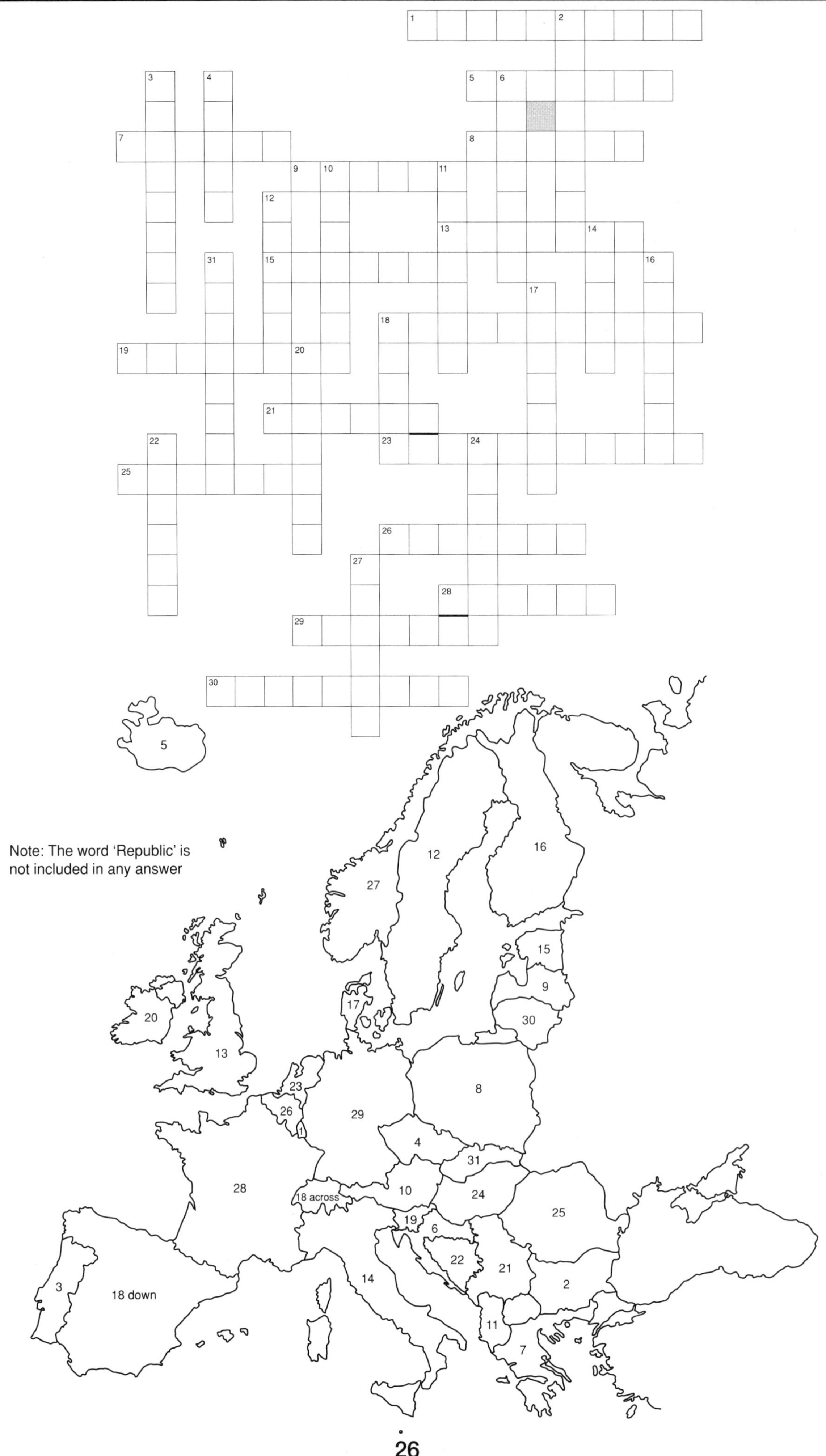
Note: The word 'Republic' is not included in any answer
18 across
18 down

Q24 - American countries (1)

8
16
3
14
10 across
6
2
15
18
12

19
10 down
7
17 across
13
11
1 across
1 down
4
5
17 down
9

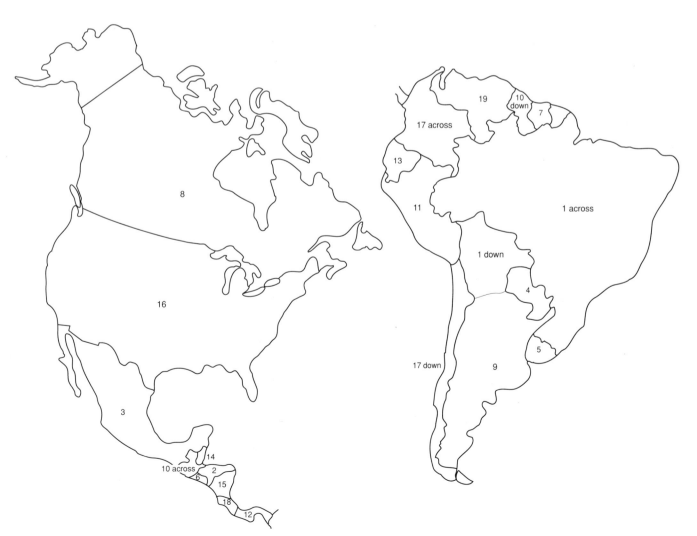

Q25 - American capitals (1)

The answers are capital cities of the countries listed.

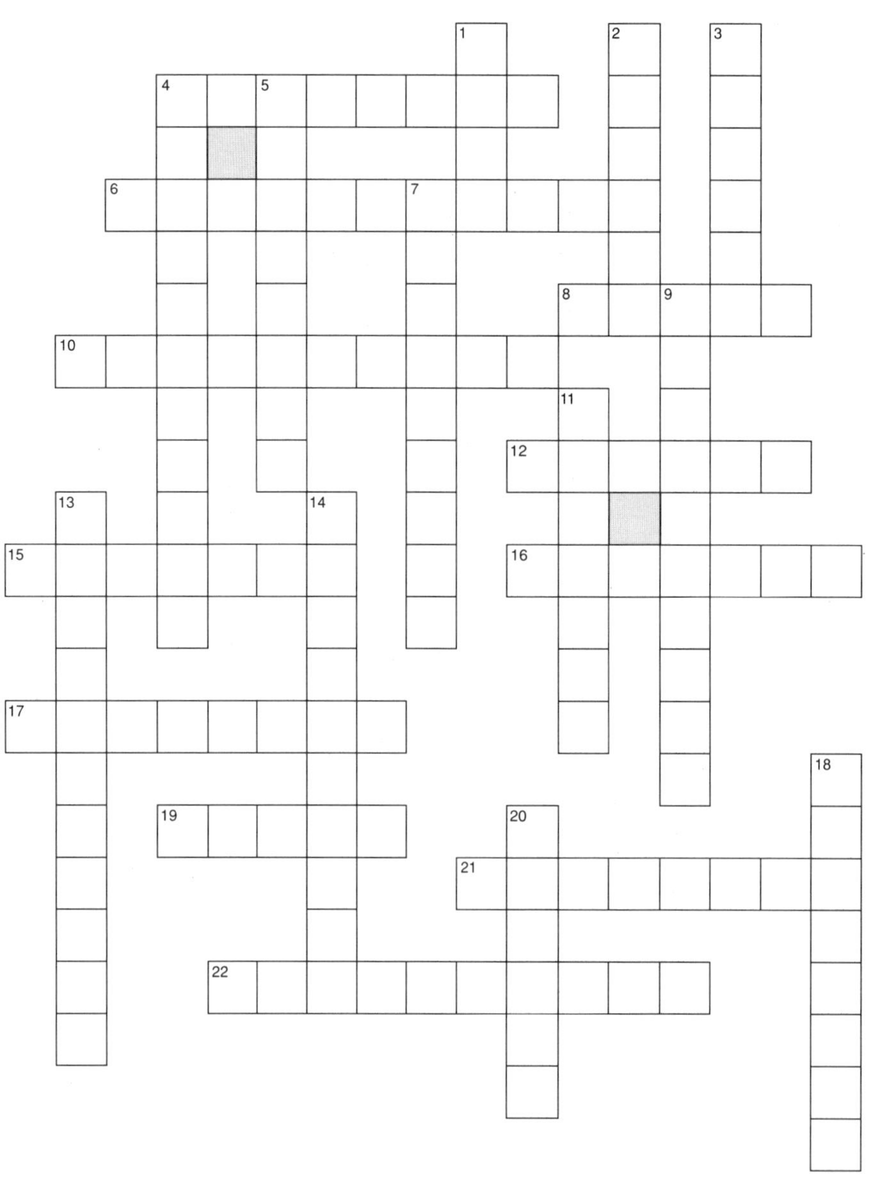

1	Peru	12	Panama
2	Canada	13	El Salvador
3	Colombia	14	Guyana
4 (across)	Brazil	15	French Guiana
4 (down)	Argentina	16	Venezuela
5	Paraguay	17	Chile
6	Honduras	18	Costa Rica
7	Guatemala	19	Ecuador
8	Bolivia	20	Mexico
9	Surinam (Dutch Guiana)	21	Belize
10	USA	22	Uruguay
11	Nicaragua		

Q26 - Great lakes of the world (1)

The answers are lakes to be found at the given latitudes and longitudes.

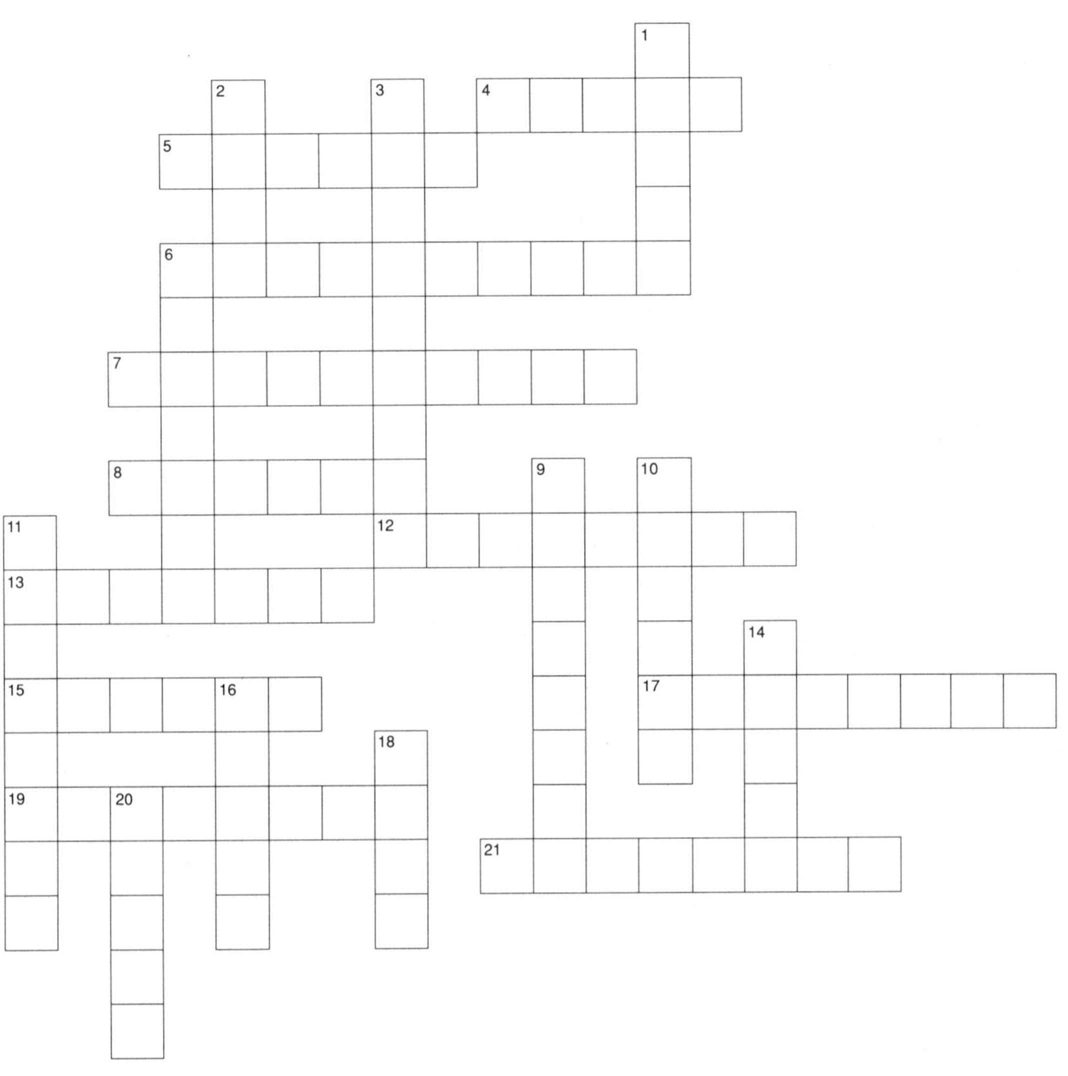

1	7° N, 0° E
2	12° N, 37° E
3	41° N, 112° W (5,4)
4	45° N, 82° W
5	58° N, 13° E
6 (across)	6° S, 30° E
6 (down)	4° N, 36° E
7	62° N, 113° W (5,5)
8	53° N, 108° E
9	1° S, 33° E
10	12° S, 34° E
11	12° N, 104° E (5,3)
12	16° S, 69° W
13	44° N, 78° W
14	61° N, 36° E
15	61° N, 31° E
16	46° N, 11° E
17	53° N, 98° W
18	42° N, 81° W
19	48° N, 88° W
20	19° S, 67° W
21	47° N, 75° E

Q27 - British rivers (1)

The answers are rivers that flow through the named towns.

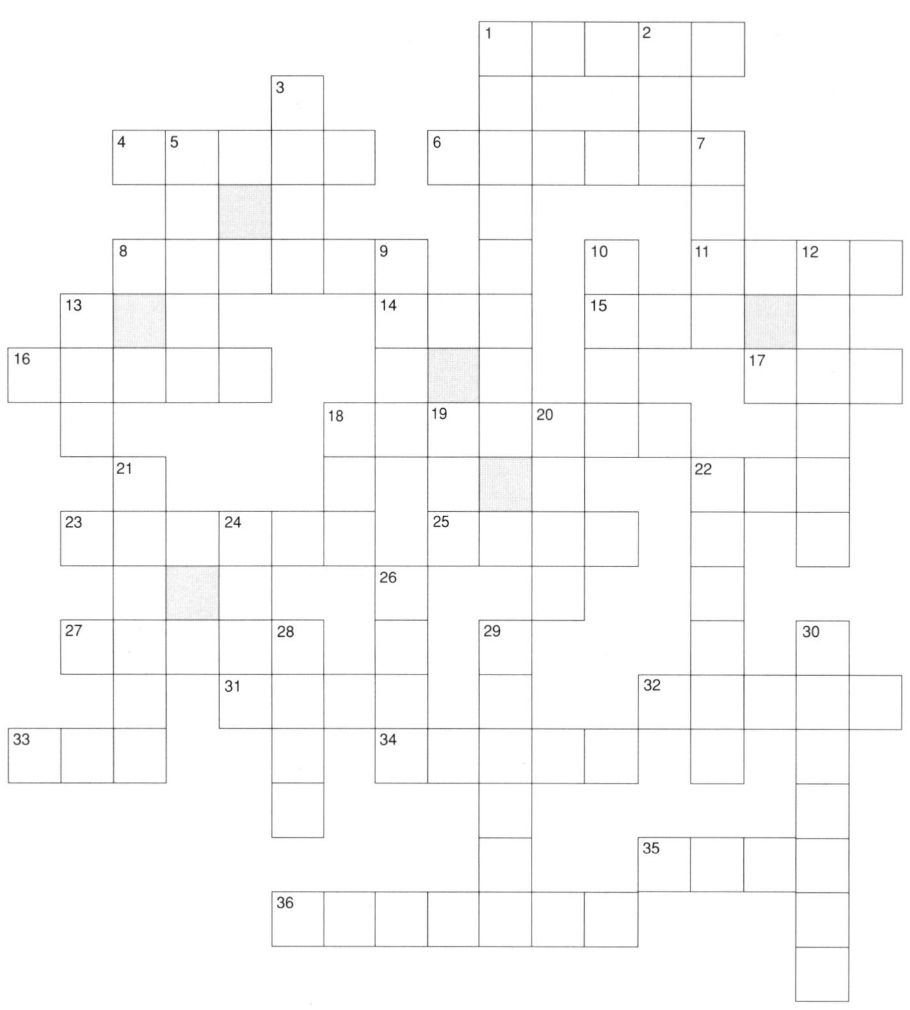

1 (across)	Glasgow	13	Doncaster	24	Aviemore
1 (down)	Banbury	14	Exeter	25	Stratford
2	Chester	15	Aberdeen	26	Stockton
3	Kings Lynn	16	Stirling	27	Berwick
4	Canterbury	17	Barnstaple	28	Totnes
5	Nottingham	18 (across)	Spalding	29	Wetherby
6	Newbury	18 (down)	Guildford	30	Bridgwater
7	Newcastle	19	Cheshunt	31	Yarmouth
8	Worcester	20	Bristol	32	Plymouth
9	Peterborough	21	Maidstone	33	Perth
10	Carlisle	22 (across)	Hereford	34	Richmond
11	Dumfries	22 (down)	Lincoln	35	Preston
12	London	23	Liverpool	36	Derby

Q28 - The weather station (1)

The clues refer to weather elements, instruments or maps.

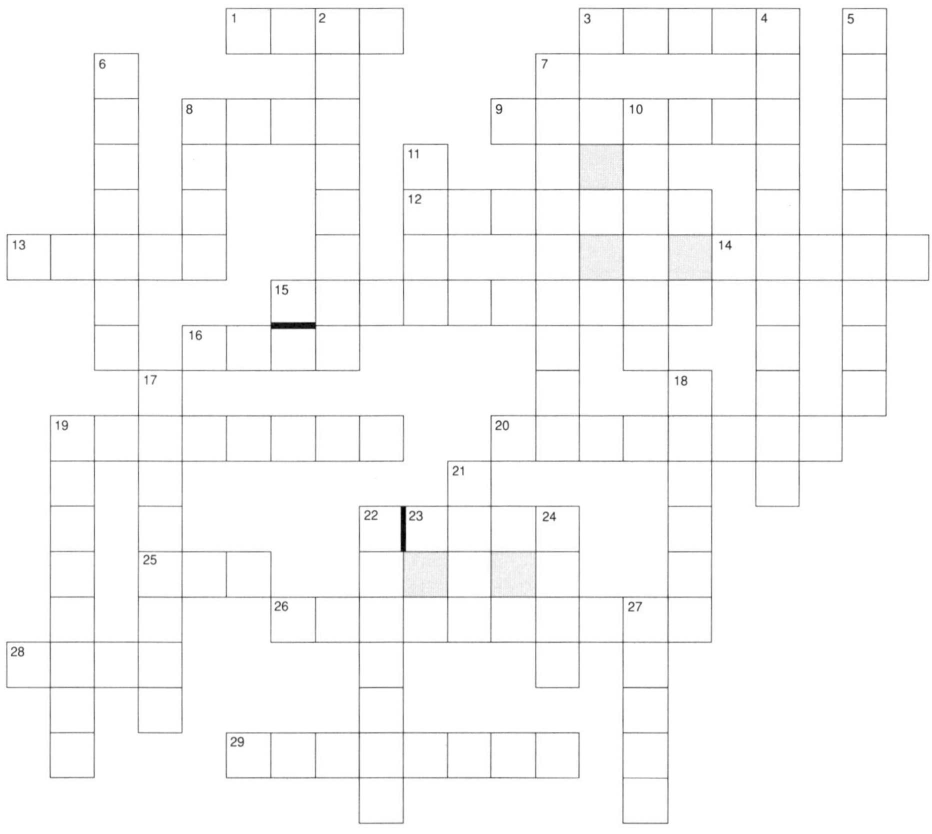

1	Visibility between 1000 and 2000m
2	Measured in hours
3	Occurs when temperature falls below 0° C
4	The measure of warmth or cold
5	This sort of screen shields some instruments
6	Metal found in thermometers
7	Instrument for measuring pressure
8 (across)	Liquid precipitation
8 (down)	Granular precipitation on trees etc.
9	The highest or greatest reading
10	Line of equal sunshine
11	Wind-speed of 0m/sec
12	Liquid found in some thermometers
13	Used for collecting 8 across
14	Boundary between air masses - can be cold or warm
15	Instrument for measuring wind speed
16	Used to show wind direction
17	Measured in a 13 and occurs along a 14
18	Line of equal pressure
19 (across)	Admiral of the winds
19 (down)	Intense fall of 24 with strong winds
20	Measured by 7
21	The movement of air measured by 15
22	Line of equal rainfall
23	U-shaped thermometer
24	Solid precipitation in hexagonal forms
25	Visibility less than 1000 m
26	Measured in eighths (5,5)
27	Temperature measured by a thermometer placed in the ground
28	Solid precipitation in lumps of ice
29	Prediction of the weather on radio or TV

Q29 - English counties

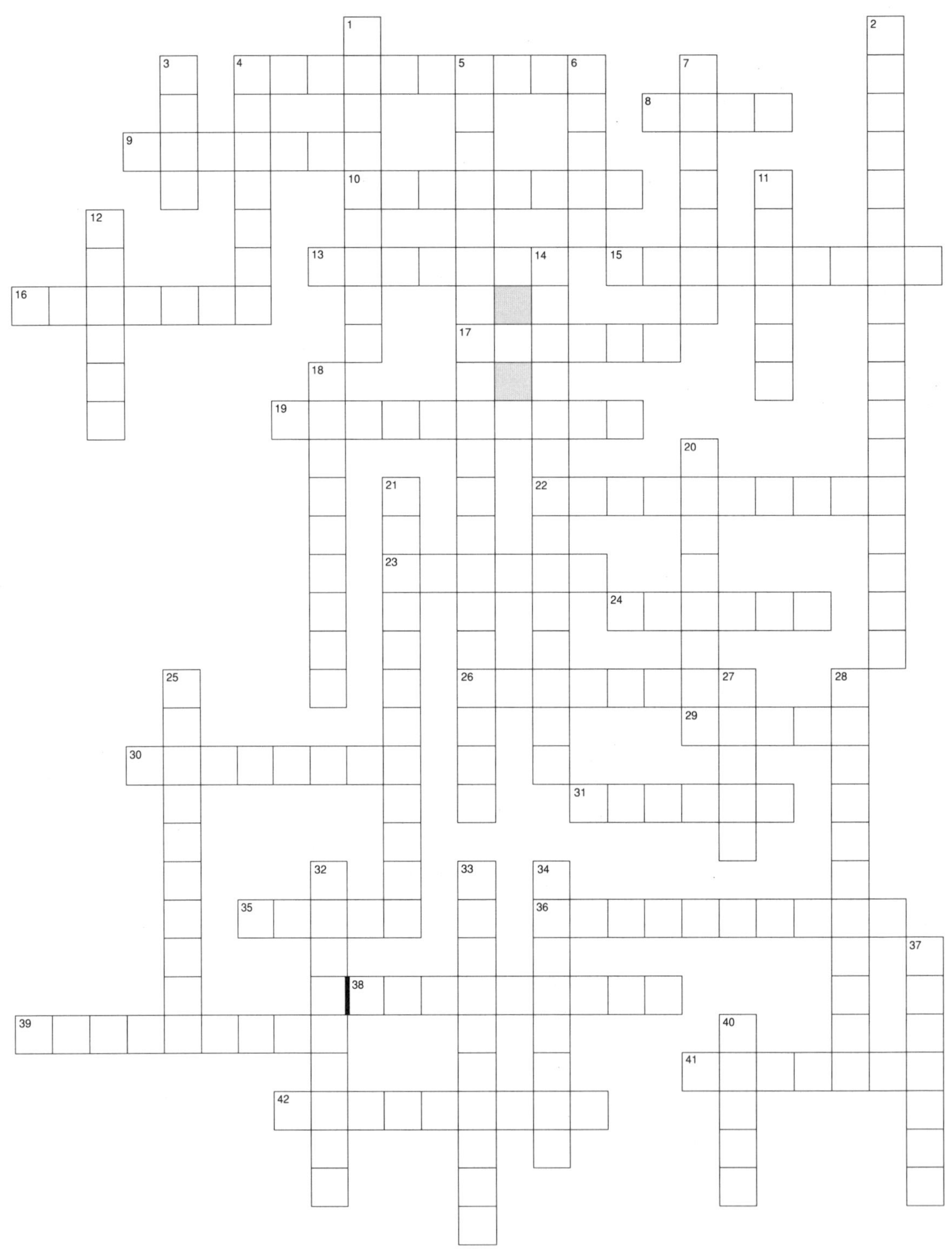

Q29 - English counties (continued)

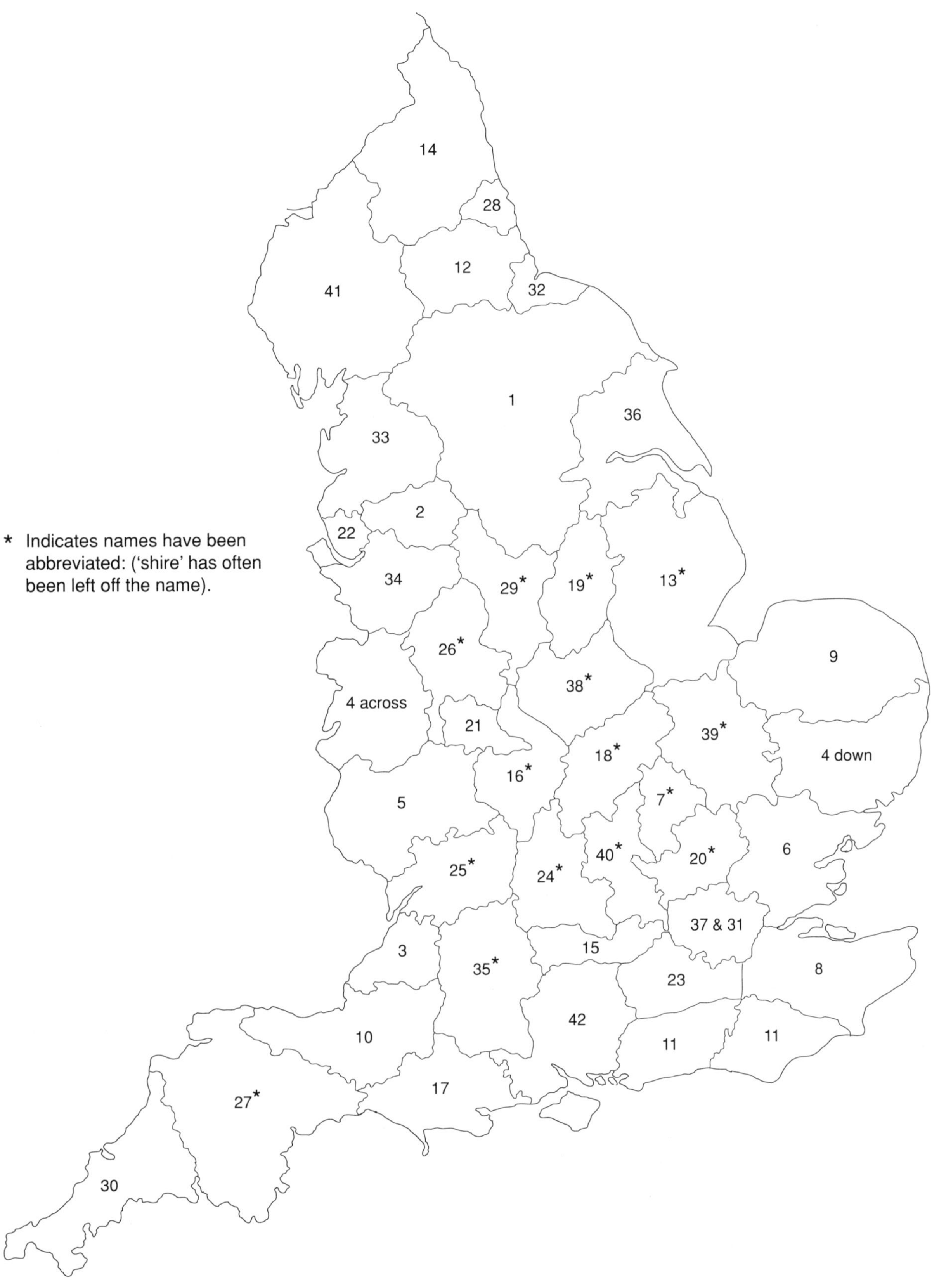

* Indicates names have been abbreviated: ('shire' has often been left off the name).

Q30 - Capitals quiz

The clues below are all about the names of capital cities. Try to find out the 32 cities and write their names beside the clues. Use whatever help you need. The letters in brackets identify the continent: E - Europe, Af - Africa, As - Asia, SA - South America, Am - rest of America, Au - Australasia.

1 Built on seven hills (E) ____________________

2 Horse ridden by Wellington at Waterloo (E) ____________________

3 What sprouts here? (E) ____________________

4 Do they bury vehicles here? (Af) ____________________

5 Dedicated to St. James (SA) ____________________

6 Called 'The Venice of the North' (E) ____________________

7 Sounds as if they are all crazy here (SA) ____________________

8 Where they put father in a sack? (As) ____________________

9 Designed by Lutyens (As) ____________________

10 Three capitals on the Equator (SA,Af) __________ __________ __________

11 Heavy weight belonging to a Queen's husband (Am) ____________________

12 Where cigars come from (Am) ____________________

13 Rope or brown paper envelopes (As) ____________________

14 Small oriental dog with change of tail (As) ____________________

15 May my right hand lose its cunning if I forget you .. (As) ____________________

16 2 Samuel 8 verse 5 (As) ____________________

17 Means 'Good airs' (SA) ____________________

18 Held the 1988 Olympics (As) ____________________

19 Dominated by the Parthenon (E) ____________________

20 Two capitals on longitude 0° (E,Af) __________ __________

21 Is this capital made of plaster? (E) ____________________

22 Two towns on either side of the Danube make this city (E) ____________________

23 Is this town multiplying by two? (E) ____________________

24 Home of the waltz (E) ____________________

25 Do you not need to pay for anything here? (Af) ____________________

26 Named after a President of the United States (Af) ____________________

27 Very hot pepper from here (SA) ____________________

28 Did this one get the boot? (Au) ____________________

29 Queen, 1837-1901 (As) ____________________

30 Capital city and state - smallest country in the world (E) ____________________

Q31 - A town square

The answers start at 1 and go clockwise round the square, working towards the centre. The last letter of each word becomes the first letter of the next word.

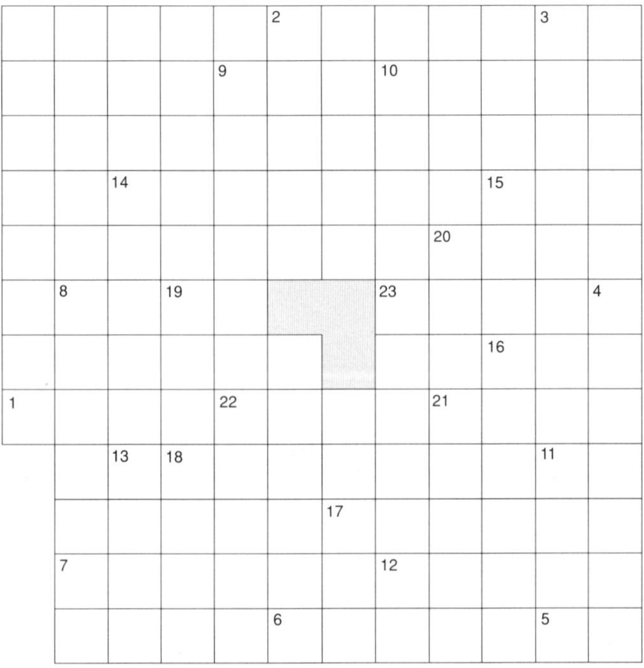

1 Secondary industry (13)
2 Area of town where a minority (originally Jews) lives (6)
3 Workplace of many in and around the CBD (7)
4 Do-it-yourself housing in Third World cities (8)
5 Housing is often distinguished by this type of class (6)
6 In a line (6)
7 Development along a main road (6)
8 First designated by Act in 1947, there are now about 30 in Britain (3,5)
9 Run-down overcrowded building or area (4)
10 Several cities all joined together, especially east-coast USA (11)
11 The outer area of a town (6)
12 The Central District is for this (8)
13 Hoyt divided towns by these (6)
14 A long word for houses, flats, etc. (10)
15 A place to buy things (4)
16 A city many times larger than any other in the country (7)
17 Suburb area detached from and outside town (5)
18 Green ones exist round some towns (4)
19 Without this towns would grind to a halt (9)
20 Larger than a village, smaller than a conurbation (4)
21 The core around which a town grew (7)
22 Unauthorised occupier of property (8)
23 A town serves this area around it (6)

Q32 - Missing vowels

The answers are all names of countries with 4 or 5 letters.
The vowels have been removed. What are the countries ?

1 ND ______	2 RN ______	3 CB ______
4 PR ______	5 RQ ______	6 ZR ______
7 ML ______	8 TG ______	9 TLY ______
10 CHL ______	11 CNG ______	12 BNN ______
13 CHN ______	14 SDN ______	15 LS ______

Q33 - Anagram countries (1)

Re-arrange the letters to form the names of the countries.

1 RAIN ______	2 MAIL ______	3 LAITY ______
4 RAISY ______	5 PLANE ______	6 SPRUCY ______
7 CHAIN ______	8 ASPIN ______	9 LOOSETH ______
10 ARKMEND ______	11 LINDEAC ______	12 PURE ______
13 WAILMA ______	14 YUHRANG ______	15 DENEWS ______

Q34 - Anagram countries (2)

Re-arrange the letters to form the names of the countries.

1 AHANG ______	2 BLAZIR ______	3 YUTREK ______
4 DOLANP ______	5 IWANTA ______	6 ADUNGA ______
7 ROADUCE ______	8 TROGUPAL ______	9 REDIALN ______
10 BIVIOLA ______	11 REGALIA ______	12 COMOAN ______
13 RUMBA ______	14 ARIZE ______	15 APISTANK ______

Q35 - British rivers (2)

Look at a map of Britain and try to work out which ones are shown here.

M = Mouth

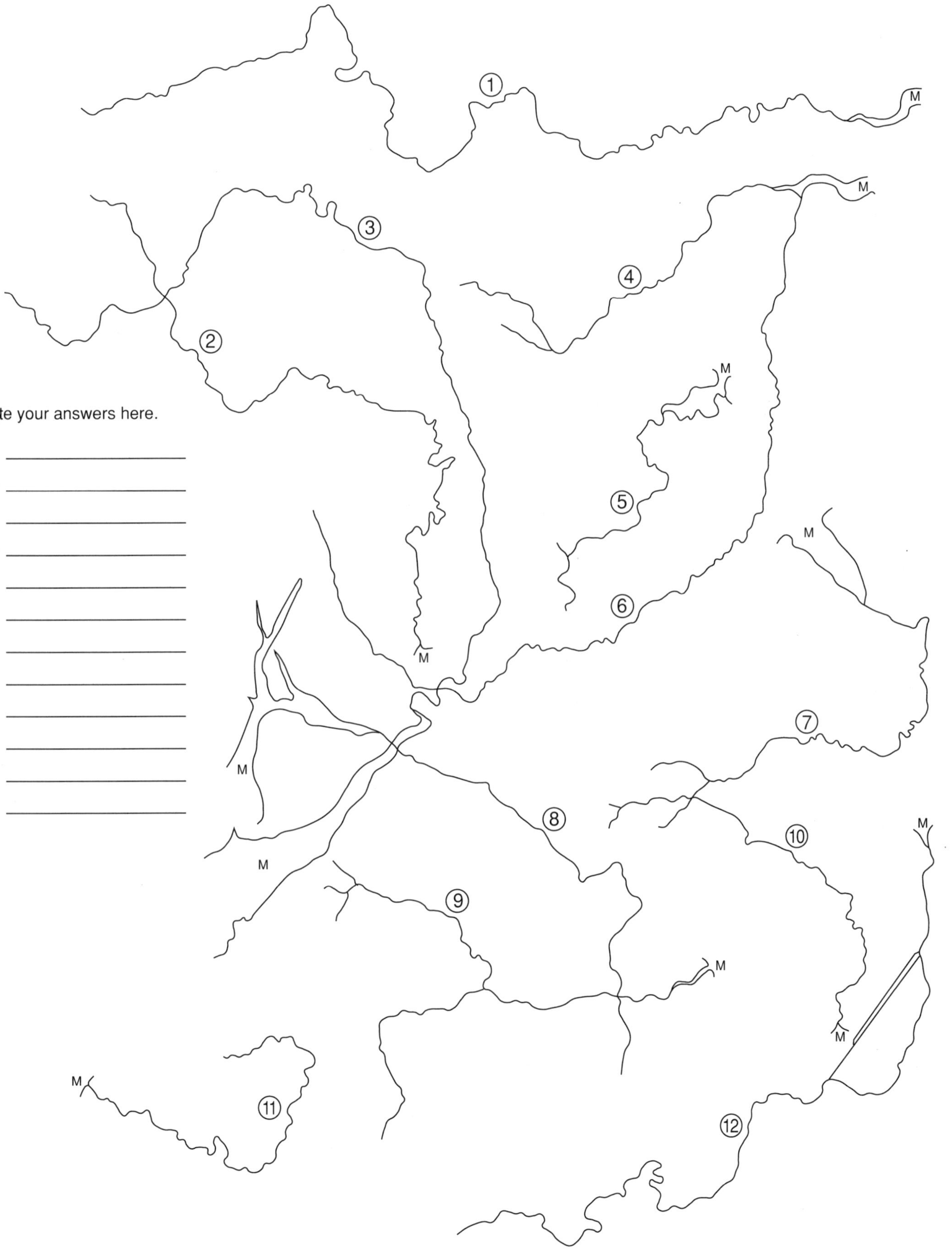

te your answers here.

Q36 - European countries (2)

Using a map of Europe work out which countries are shown here. (They are not shown to scale.)

Write your answers here.

1 ____________________

2 ____________________

3 ____________________

4 ____________________

5 ____________________

6 ____________________

7 ____________________

8 ____________________

Q37 - South American countries

Using a map of South America try to work out which countries are shown here. (They are not shown to scale.)

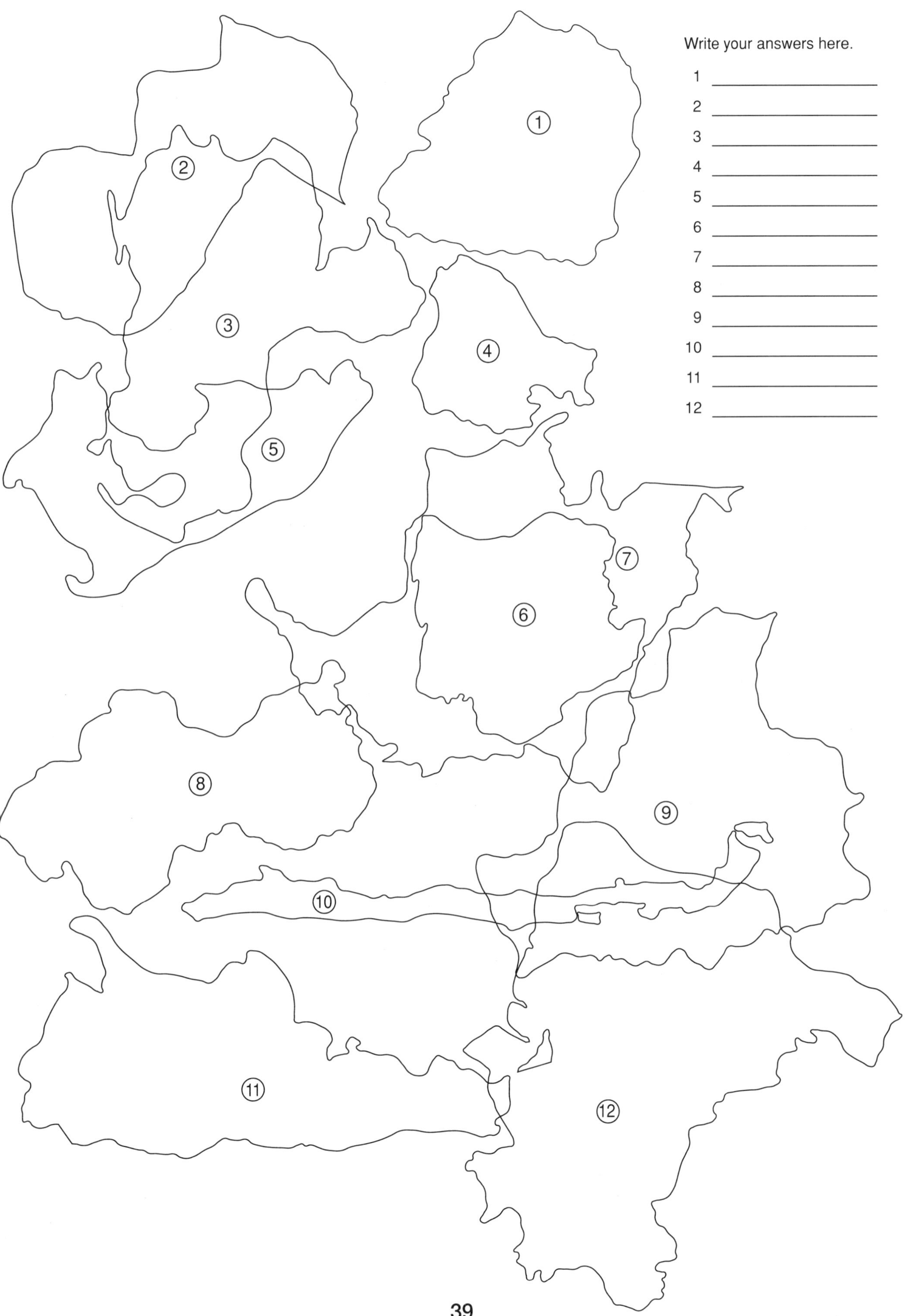

Write your answers here.

1 ______________________

2 ______________________

3 ______________________

4 ______________________

5 ______________________

6 ______________________

7 ______________________

8 ______________________

9 ______________________

10 ______________________

11 ______________________

12 ______________________

Q38 - Tectonics

Find and ring the listed words. The remaining letters spell out the names of eight oceans and seas.

S H I E L D Y E L L A V C P A M R
U C O R E L E R E H P S O H T I L
B C R I G A T T F A I C N A F D A
D T L U A I I R N N N T T T I O U
U V Y C S S N G E I A N I F D C R
C O N E E T A L P N E M N I N E A
T L I D B E R A A N C O E R O A S
I C N A A M G A M R O H N D T N I
O A C T S U N A M I T O T E U R A
N N S I A C A A V A L W O L L I P
Z O I S L A N D A R C N T T P D A
O R M C T T I C A N A W D N O G Y
N I A T N U O M D L O F E A L E L
E A R T H Q U A K E O W B M L A C
K C A R E R E H P S O N E H T S A
B E N I O F F Z O N E I B B E A N
T E C T O N I C T R A N S F O R M

ANDESITE
ASTHENOSPHERE
BASALT
BENIOFF ZONE
CONE
CONTINENT
CORE
CRUST
DRIFT
EARTHQUAKE
FOLD MOUNTAIN
GAP
GONDWANA
GRANITE
GUYOT
ISLAND ARC
LAURASIA
LITHOSPHERE
MAGMA
MANTLE
MID-OCEAN RIDGE
MOHO
OCEAN
PANGAEA
PILLOW LAVA
PLATE
PLUTON
RIFT
SHIELD
SIAL
SIMA
SUBDUCTION ZONE
TECTONIC
TRANSFORM
TRENCH
TSUNAMI
VALLEY
VOLCANO

Write your answers here.

1 ____________________
2 ____________________
3 ____________________
4 ____________________
5 ____________________
6 ____________________
7 ____________________
8 ____________________

Q39 - Volcanic activity

Find and ring the listed words. The remaining letters spell out the names of seven volcanoes.

L A V A P L A T E A U V C D C
A H E C I M U P X E S U O O R
C T I T P L U G T V I U N M A
C I N I E S E A I T M E E E T
O L A V A Y H S N N L A R B E
L O E E S E H O C E E U G O R
I P T E N I N A T V S K A M L
T O R I E S L T A S H R Y B A
H L P L O D M L I A P B O D K
L S D I E F U F U M A R O L E
J I P R A S U L P H U R I R A
C P A H O E H O E U M T I N N
S T E A M C O O N A C L O V G
N U E E A R D E N T E T O P A
X I H E K L A T I L L I P A L

AA
ACTIVE
ASH
BOMB
CALDERA
CONE
CONELET
CRATER LAKE
DOME
DORMANT
DYKE
EXTINCT
FISSURE
FUMAROLE
GAS
GEYSER
HOT SPRING
LACCOLITH
LAPILLI
LAVA
LAVA PLATEAU
LOPOLITH
MAGMA
NUEE ARDENTE
PAHOEHOE
PIPE
PLUG
PUMICE
SHIELD
SILL
SPINE
STEAM
SULPHUR
VEIN
VENT
VOLCANO

Write your answers here.

1 ____________ 5 ____________
2 ____________ 6 ____________
3 ____________ 7 ____________
4 ____________

Q40 - Folds and faults

Find and ring the listed words. The remaining letters spell out the names of three American mountains.

A S A P P R A C S T L U A F N
T T E O V E R T H R U S T A A
S E N P H A E R L P A T N U C
E P I D C O O V T H I N A L I
U F L D A W R H A D E E P T R
C A C O L T R S L E T M P B O
A U N W N O S O T A H E E L M
N L Y N W C F E L A R C S O R
T T S T B C A P R A O A N C A
I D O U M R U S U C W L E K O
C P E R I C L I N E E P B S V
L A G N L D T X I N I S A B E
I M R O F S N A R T F I R R R
N T I L T B L O C K O D G N F
E N I L C N Y S T R I K E D O
C O M P R E S S I O N A C K L
T E N S I O N D L O F N W O D

ANTICLINE
ARMORICAN
AXIS
BASIN
COMPRESSION
CREST
CUESTA
DIP
DISPLACEMENT
DOWNFOLD
DOWNTURN
FAULT
FAULT BLOCK
FAULT SCARP
FOLD
GEOSYNCLINE
GRABEN
HADE
HEAVE
HORST
LIMB
NAPPE
OVERFOLD
OVERTHRUST
PERICLINE
PLATEAU
RIFT
STEP FAULT
STRIKE
SYNCLINE
TEAR
TENSION
THROW (x2)
TILTBLOCK
TRANSFORM
UPFOLD
UPTHROW

Write your answers here.

1 ____________ 3 ____________
2 ____________

Q41 - Soils

Find and ring the listed words. The remaining letters spell out the names of three more soil types.

F	B	R	O	W	N	E	A	R	T	H	A	E	R
R	A	S	R	H	T	R	A	E	K	C	A	L	B
E	S	O	L	O	D	U	A	N	I	L	L	G	H
T	I	L	Z	E	S	T	S	D	I	A	T	R	U
A	C	O	O	I	O	X	I	Z	I	Y	E	A	M
W	C	T	N	R	I	E	E	I	L	H	L	V	U
D	S	H	A	I	L	T	R	N	O	O	I	E	S
N	S	T	L	A	I	O	O	A	A	R	F	L	E
U	C	H	E	R	N	O	Z	E	M	I	O	O	I
O	L	O	E	P	N	Y	E	L	G	Z	R	P	R
R	C	T	A	E	P	H	M	A	K	O	P	E	E
G	A	N	W	A	T	E	R	S	A	N	D	D	S
L	Z	C	I	K	C	O	R	T	N	E	R	A	P
S	O	R	H	E	G	N	I	H	C	A	E	L	S
I	N	T	R	A	Z	O	N	A	L	T	N	F	U
L	A	P	O	D	S	O	L	A	C	O	D	E	P
T	L	T	E	R	R	A	R	O	S	S	A	R	T

ACID
AIR
AZONAL
BASIC
BLACK EARTH
BROWN EARTH
CLAY
CHERNOZEM
GLEY
GRAVEL
GROUNDWATER
HORIZON
HUMUS
INTRAZONAL
IRON PAN
LATERITE
LEACHING
LOAM
PARENT ROCK
PEAT
PEDALFER
PEDOCAL
PODSOL
PRAIRIE
PROFILE
RENDZINA
SAND
SERIES
SIEROZEM
SILT
SOIL
SOLOD
SOLOTH
STEPPE
TERRA ROSSA
TEXTURE
WATER
ZONAL

Write your answers here.

1 ____________ 3 ____________

2 ____________

Q42 - Deserts

Find and ring the listed words. The remaining letters spell out the names of six major deserts.

M	U	S	H	R	O	O	M	R	O	C	K	S	E
D	R	A	A	A	A	L	E	H	N	A	R	N	X
A	N	L	M	F	S	G	O	A	A	T	M	I	F
P	I	I	A	I	I	B	H	E	N	U	D	A	O
A	L	N	D	E	S	C	M	E	S	A	T	L	L
A	C	A	A	S	R	A	M	M	T	S	A	P	I
S	W	Q	Y	A	O	I	N	O	R	T	A	R	A
I	N	U	B	A	D	L	A	N	D	S	U	E	T
N	R	I	R	E	S	N	E	G	U	E	Z	B	I
O	G	F	P	O	Y	A	R	D	A	N	G	B	O
F	D	E	F	L	A	T	I	O	N	B	I	I	N
A	B	R	A	S	I	O	N	M	H	O	J	G	A
T	V	G	D	O	O	L	F	H	S	A	L	F	E
B	A	J	A	D	A	N	A	I	S	E	T	R	A

ABRASION
AQUIFER
ARTESIAN
BADLANDS
BAJADA
BARCHAN
BUTTE
DEFLATION
DRAA
DUNE
ERG
EXFOLIATION
FAN
FLASH FLOOD
GIBBER PLAIN
HAMADA
HORN
LOESS
MESA
MUSHROOM ROCK
OASIS
PEDIMENT
PLAYA
REG
SALINA
SEIF
SERIR
TAFONI
WADI
YARDANG
ZEUGEN

Write your answers here.

1 ____________ 4 ____________

2 ____________ 5 ____________

3 ____________ 6 ____________

Q43 - Glaciation

Find and ring the listed words. The remaining letters spell out seven areas where glaciers are found today.

R I B B O N L A K E G T F I R D R R
O E E N M L U I A L Y C I T A R R E
C O R R I E C N N I E W D A L U T I
H R A N S E L T A P L M A R L M R C
E M A K A R E T E T L R C N A L U A
M O E G T C C R E V A S S E F I N L
O R E I A S N O U T V K E V E N C G
U A H O R N E B O U L D E R C L A Y
T I F I O R D K C W A T E R I N T E
O N A H N O I T A V I N I M A O E L
N E L A Y A S G A L C A L L P I D L
N S A N W O N S D I A E O S R S S A
E H A N G I N G V A L L E Y O A P V
E C K I K E T T L E G E S S F R U E
N N I C E S H E E T O S S C A B R N
A T U O N S O U T W A S H P L A I N
A L L U V I A L F A N D E U Q R I C
P I P A N A H C O L D N A K C O N K

ABRASION
ALLUVIAL FAN
ALP
ARETE
BOULDER CLAY
CIRQUE
CORRIE
CRAG AND TAIL
CREVASSE
CWM
DRIFT
DRUMLIN
ERRATIC
ESKER
FIORD
GLACIAL VALLEY
HANGING VALLEY
HORN
ICE AGE
ICEFALL
ICE SHEET
KAME
KETTLE
KNOCK AND LOCHAN
LAKES
LIP
LOESS
MELT
MORAINE
NEVE
NIVATION
NUNATAK
OUTWASH PLAIN
PLUCKING
RIBBON LAKE
ROCHE MOUTONNEE
SCREE
SNOUT (x2)
SNOW
TARN
TRUNCATED SPUR
VALLEY GLACIER
WATER

Write your answers here.

1 ____________________

2 ____________________

3 ____________________

4 ____________________

5 ____________________

6 ____________________

7 ____________________

Q44 - Limestone (2)

Find and ring the listed words. The remaining letters spell out the names of three British caves.

C	O	C	K	P	I	T	W	S	P	R	I	N	G	S
A	O	O	L	I	M	E	S	T	O	N	E	O	K	I
R	T	C	L	I	N	T	M	A	S	S	I	V	E	N
B	E	D	D	I	N	G	P	L	A	N	E	E	Y	K
O	R	P	N	S	T	A	L	A	C	T	I	T	E	T
N	R	O	R	E	S	E	P	G	I	E	M	U	H	S
I	A	T	E	N	E	E	K	M	P	O	L	J	E	R
C	R	H	V	I	G	J	O	I	N	T	D	W	A	A
A	O	O	A	L	R	L	E	T	R	C	H	A	L	K
C	S	L	C	O	O	M	B	E	L	G	L	D	A	A
I	S	E	N	D	G	N	I	R	P	S	C	A	V	E
D	A	E	C	N	E	G	R	U	S	E	R	Y	U	R
S	W	A	L	L	O	W	H	O	L	E	O	G	O	F

BEDDING PLANE
CARBONIC ACID
CAVE
CAVERN
CHALK
CLINT
COCKPIT
COOMBE
DOLINE
DOLOMITE
GORGE
GRIKE
HUM
JOINT
KARST
LIMESTONE
MASSIVE
OOLITE
POLJE
POTHOLE
RESURGENCE
SINK
SPRING (x2)
STALACTITE
STALAGMITE
SWALLOW HOLE
TERRA ROSSA
UVALA

Write your answers here.

1 ____________ 3 ____________

2 ____________

Q45 - Rivers (2)

Find and ring the listed words. The remaining letters spell out the names of eight major rivers.

D	R	A	I	N	A	G	E	B	A	S	I	N	I
E	M	I	S	F	L	O	O	D	P	L	A	I	N
G	O	R	G	E	L	O	H	T	O	P	S	I	C
R	E	D	N	A	E	M	I	X	S	S	S	I	I
A	L	R	N	P	P	D	B	I	N	A	P	I	S
D	B	L	E	I	E	O	A	G	B	A	R	D	E
I	O	N	G	J	W	E	S	R	E	S	I	E	D
N	W	I	W	L	U	E	E	N	R	P	N	N	M
G	D	U	A	S	S	V	L	Y	A	O	G	D	E
C	D	K	T	A	I	E	E	R	N	G	C	R	A
A	E	T	E	R	L	L	V	N	Z	C	Y	I	N
N	L	E	R	L	L	L	E	O	A	W	A	T	D
Y	T	M	A	Z	E	O	L	N	W	T	Y	I	E
O	A	T	E	R	R	A	C	E	S	E	E	C	R
N	O	I	T	A	T	R	O	P	S	N	A	R	T

BASE LEVEL
CANYON
CORRADE
DEGRADING
DELTA
DENDRITIC
DRAINAGE BASIN
ELBOW
FLOOD PLAIN
GORGE
INCISED MEANDER
LEVEE
MEANDER
OX-BOW LAKE
POTHOLE
RAPIDS
REJUVENATE
RIVER BASIN
SPRING
TERRACES
TRANSPORTATION
TRELLIS
WATER
WIND

Write your answers here.

1 ____________ 5 ____________

2 ____________ 6 ____________

3 ____________ 7 ____________

4 ____________ 8 ____________

Q46 - Coasts (2)

Find and ring the listed words. The remaining letters spell out the names of five seas.

L H R A B E R O H S F F O
O M C E R D E L T A I L D
N I T R E E M O A T O L L
G R E V A W R R A B R I N
S R A B K M O E M A D S A
H C N E E X F O T C B L N
O L N A R A T S C K K A A
R B O C A L A T T W R N I
E L O H W O L B U A I D T
D C G N C O P R C S C T A
R I A H T I D E E H A K M
I C L I F F D R V S E I L
F A P P M U T S A O E A A
T S T I C H S A W S C A D

ARCH
ATOLL
BACKWASH
BAR
BEACH
BLOWHOLE
BREAKER
CAVE
CLIFF
COAST
COVE
DALMATIAN
DELTA
FIORD
HEAD
ISLAND
LAGOON
LONGSHORE DRIFT
OFFSHORE BAR
PLATFORM
RACE
RIA
SEA
SPIT
STACK
STORM
STUMP
SWASH
TIDE
TOMBOLO
WAVE
WAVE-CUT

Write your answers here.

1 ____________ 4 ____________
2 ____________ 5 ____________
3 ____________

Q47 - Clouds and rain (2)

Find and ring the listed words. The remaining letters spell out the names of nine places with unusual climates.

C O N D E N S A T I O N W A I
U F O G A O M L E S D I A L E
M V I E R I K U S H U A O R Y
U A T N S S S K L C O R H E E
L R C T R S W A E O L L R L P
O U E R N E J I E V C A A I O
N S V A D R S T T O K T I E C
I T N I O P W E D D L N N F I
M O O N E E A T H S I O S R H
B R C V A D L T L U G R H A P
U M E Y D L I A H L H F A I A
S T R A T U S A I U T L D N R
L O L Y N U M A G M N A O L G
A Z D O O L F I H U I D W Z O
I T N O R F D L O C N Y E A R
W A R M F R O N T H G B O R O

CIRRUS
CLOUD
COLD FRONT
COLUMN
CONDENSATION
CONVECTION
CUMULONIMBUS
CUMULUS
DEPRESSION
DEW
DEW POINT
FLOOD
FOG
FRONT
FRONTAL RAIN
HAIL
HIGH
LIGHTNING
MIST
OROGRAPHIC
RAIN
RAINSHADOW
RELIEF RAIN
SLEET
STORM
STRATUS
THUNDER
WARM FRONT

Write your answers here.

1 ____________ 6 ____________
2 ____________ 7 ____________
3 ____________ 8 ____________
4 ____________ 9 ____________
5 ____________

Q48 - Lakes

Find and ring the listed words. The remaining letters spell out the names of seven large lakes.

B	O	U	L	D	E	R	C	L	A	Y	S	M	U	P	G	B
D	E	K	C	O	L	B	A	V	A	L	T	E	E	R	N	A
I	M	G	N	I	T	L	U	A	F	O	A	T	R	M	I	R
F	R	O	C	K	B	A	S	I	N	H	R	E	N	R	P	R
D	L	T	R	O	U	G	H	I	A	O	N	O	A	I	R	I
C	E	A	H	A	I	O	G	F	U	X	B	R	Y	F	A	E
S	I	F	S	A	I	O	F	G	N	B	H	I	A	T	W	R
A	R	U	L	H	R	N	H	O	I	O	N	T	L	V	T	C
L	R	O	C	A	L	D	E	R	A	W	N	E	P	A	S	I
T	O	T	A	R	T	I	O	D	O	M	D	C	A	L	U	N
L	C	L	A	W	I	I	B	E	A	V	E	R	V	L	R	O
A	C	R	A	T	E	R	O	I	S	M	A	A	R	E	C	T
K	S	O	L	U	T	I	O	N	I	C	M	T	T	Y	O	C
E	R	L	A	V	A	S	U	B	S	I	D	E	N	C	E	E
K	E	T	T	L	E	H	O	L	E	I	A	R	D	N	E	T
G	N	I	D	L	O	F	S	S	L	A	N	D	S	L	I	P

BARRIER	LAVA BLOCKED
BEAVER	LAVA SUBSIDENCE
BOULDER CLAY	MAAR
CALDERA	METEORITE CRAT
CORRIE	MORAINE DAMME
CRATER	OASIS
CRUST WARPING	OXBOW
DEFLATION	PLAYA
DELTA	RIBBON
FAULTING	RIFT VALLEY
FLASH	ROCK BASIN
FOLDING	SALT LAKE
HAFF	SOLUTION
KETTLE HOLE	TARN
LAGOON	TECTONIC
LANDSLIP	TROUGH (x2)

Write your answers here.

1 ______________ 5 ______________
2 ______________ 6 ______________
3 ______________ 7 ______________
4 ______________

Q49 - Tropical areas

Find and ring the listed words. The remaining letters spell out the names of nine African rivers.

G	R	O	U	N	D	N	U	T	S	B	A	B	O	A	B
R	N	S	I	Z	N	E	L	L	H	T	E	L	L	I	M
A	E	O	M	N	E	O	L	I	I	A	S	A	M	G	E
S	R	R	A	A	A	B	T	E	P	O	U	E	T	A	N
S	A	E	L	R	G	A	U	T	P	V	N	S	T	O	L
L	T	C	L	B	L	C	A	M	O	H	G	N	A	S	Z
A	D	O	E	E	U	A	A	A	P	C	A	T	T	L	E
N	R	N	E	Z	M	C	S	N	O	T	A	N	I	L	F
D	A	I	A	R	I	I	E	N	T	C	O	R	T	A	F
A	P	H	N	L	S	A	B	A	A	F	C	G	E	N	A
Z	O	R	A	A	K	U	M	V	M	E	I	A	M	O	R
B	E	E	L	Z	R	R	E	A	U	I	B	R	B	S	I
C	L	U	A	C	A	L	A	S	S	N	Z	A	E	O	G
J	U	B	S	H	D	A	E	P	O	L	E	T	N	A	T

ACACIA	LION
ANTELOPE	LLANOS
BAOBAB	MAIZE
BEANS	MALLEE
CAMPOS	MASAI
CATTLE	MILLET
COTTON	MULGA
ELEPHANT	PARKLAND
FIRE	RHINOCEROS
GIRAFFE	SAVANNA
GNU	SCRUB
GRASSLAND	SISAL
GROUNDNUTS	TOBACCO
HARMATTAN	TSETSE
HAUSA	VELD
HIPPOPOTAMUS	ZEBRA
LEOPARD	ZEBU

Write your answers here.

1 ______________ 3 ______________ 5 ______________ 7 ______________ 9 ______________
2 ______________ 4 ______________ 6 ______________ 8 ______________

Q50 - Mediterranean areas

Find and ring the listed words. The remaining letters spell out the names of nine rivers.

R O S E M A R Y D O O W D E R
E R M I G W A L N U T S N N E
U H Y O R N E O C C O R I S D
C T R J A R R A H T I S S S N
A E T B P E A A R C I B M E A
L M L P E O E K L A O O A R E
Y P E B F I G S R M R R H P L
P E V E R G R E E N O A K Y O
T R S I U Q A M O Q C N A C C
U A R N I O T N I E U O D S H
S T L E T M V H D A L O O E A
R E D N O I T A G I R R I P P
L E M O N A R R V U A J U A A
L A R T S I M E C N O A R R R
G B G O R S E U G I R R A G R
T S A O C T S E W E D I D Z A
L E V E C H E R E D N E V A L

ALMOND
BORA
BROOM
CEDAR
CHAPARRAL
CORK
CYPRESS
DROUGHT
EUCALYPTUS
EVERGREEN OAK
FIG
GARRIGUE
GORSE
GRAPEFRUIT
GRAPES
IRRIGATION
JARRAH
KARRI
KHAMSIN
LAVENDER
LEMON
LEVECHE
MAQUIS
MISTRAL
MYRTLE
OLEANDER
OLIVE
ORANGE
RAISIN
REDWOOD
ROSEMARY
SEQUOIA
SIROCCO
TEMPERATE
WALNUTS
WEST COAST

Write your answers here.

1 ____________ 6 ____________
2 ____________ 7 ____________
3 ____________ 8 ____________
4 ____________ 9 ____________
5 ____________

Q51 - Middle latitudes

Find and ring the listed words. The remaining letters spell out the names of seven European rivers.

O R O G R A P H I C D O O W D R A H L
T U N T S E H C F A E L D A O R B E S
D E P R E S S I O N E I Y T N M A W R
E R T S A O C T S E W R I H L C I A E
P O P L A R U U R B I U L E H N N R L
H T A E H N O E R A R A W I L T E M I
S O C C L U D E D F R O N T I B M C E
H A E A D L B M M O L G W C N N A U F
M E W I A M O A T L O N Y N L L E R R
B I C O I O P S I I R C E S E E B R A
K E X T R L A W D V L E R N Z A N E I
D A E E E P L T N O R F M R A W R N N
B C O L D F R O N T P E W S H E O T S
E R W A R M S E C T O R H P E E H S H

ALDER
ANTICYCLONE
ARABLE
ASH
BEECH
BROADLEAF
BROWN EARTH
CHESTNUT
COLD FRONT
DAIRY
DECIDUOUS
DEPRESSION
ELM
FRUIT
HARDWOOD
HAZEL
HEATH
HORNBEAM
LEACHING
MAPLE
MIXED
MOOR
OAK
OCCLUDED FRONT
OROGRAPHIC
PASTORAL
PODSOL
POPLAR
RELIEF RAIN
SHEEP
TIMBER
WALNUT
WARM CURRENT
WARM FRONT
WARM SECTOR
WEST COAST
WILLOW

Write your answers here.

1 ____________ 3 ____________ 5 ____________ 7 ____________
2 ____________ 4 ____________ 6 ____________

Q52 - Tropical forests

Find and ring the listed words. The remaining letters spell out the names of eight South American rivers.

G A P A R A S I T E T N A I G C

A M I B A A X Z O E N T R O C O

L E T U N O C O C A R N E T I C

L L P T A Y E E F N S M D H X K

E P I T C E N T L G O R I L L A

R P R R O C V A Y E N P P T I T

Y A D E N B O E G H P I S N E O

S E G S D S A P R O P H Y T E O

U N N S A T C N R G H I A L N K

Y I A O C O C E A A R A P N F A

E P G K B R R R O N N E M E T P

K J A R E E R I I A A R E I R I

N I A E B Y M G I B B O N N A D

O E P B I R E L I D O C O R C A

M E U M B R E L L A K I D K I D

R R N A P O E E Z N A P M I H C

ANACONDA
ANTS
BANANAS
BUTTRESS
CHIMPANZEE
COBRA
COCKATOO
COCOA
COCONUT
COPRA
CREEPER
CROCODILE
DIK-DIK
DRIPTIP
ELEPHANT
EPIPHYTE
EVERGREEN
FLYING FOX

GALLERY
GIANT
GIBBON
GORILLA
HIPPO
LIANA
MAHOGANY
MONKEY
OKAPI
PARASITE
PINEAPPLE
RUBBER
SAPROPHYTE
SNAKE
SPIDER
STOREY
TERMITE
UMBRELLA

Write your answers here.

1 ____________________

2 ____________________

3 ____________________

4 ____________________

5 ____________________

6 ____________________

7 ____________________

8 ____________________

Q53 - New towns (1)

Identify these British New Towns.

1 A well-known type of writing paper ______________________

2 Lady who appears in 'The Importance of being Earnest' __________

3 How old this boy's name is ______________________

4 Doctor missionary to Africa ______________________

5 Poet plus economist ______________________

6 First president of the USA ______________________

7 Great road builder and engineer ______________________

8 Coloured drainage channel ______________________

9 Rudely described as 'the hole with the mint in it' __________

10 Sounds like a Scot's crow ______________________

11 Jean ______ was a famous film actress ______________________

12 Childish name for an insect: creepy - ______________________

Q54 - New towns (2)

Sort out these anagrams to find names of some British New Towns.

1 THE HELPS MADE ME ______________________

2 WINDY TANGLEY CREW ______________________

3 SLAM RED LEEKS ______________________

4 TREE PEEL ______________________

5 GREEN SLOTH ______________________

6 RED KITE BASIL ______________________

7 BAD RUM UNCLE ______________________

8 WRONG TRAIN ______________________

9 TWINE FEY FALCON ______________________

10 LIFT HADE ______________________

11 TAN THORN MOP ______________________

12 BORE OTHER PUG ______________________

Q55 - Islands quiz

Find the island or island group to which each clue refers.

1 The birthplace of Napoleon ____________________

2 The island of the Minoan civilisation ____________________

3 Do they catch small fish here? ____________________

4 The George Cross island ____________________

5 Acts 13 verse 4 ____________________

6 An island associated with Puffins ____________________

7 Snaefell is the highest mountain here ____________________

8 The Cuillins are the largest feature here ____________________

9 A colossus guarded the harbour ____________________

10 Famous for cows and tomatoes ____________________

11 This island gave us the word 'serendipity' ____________________

12 Famous for giant tortoises ____________________

13 Do we get little yellow birds from here? ____________________

14 The source of sweet wine or cake ____________________

15 Island of the exile and death of Napoleon ____________________

16 Once called Van Diemen's Land ____________________

17 A two-piece swim-suit ____________________

18 Also known as the Malvinas ____________________

19 Halfway across the Pacific, so it says ____________________

20 It has giant heads on it ____________________

21 Where the Bounty mutineers ended up ____________________

22 Named after an Old Testament king ____________________

23 The home of Ulysses ____________________

24 The origin of sweaters ____________________

Q56 - Where on earth ...? (1)

These boxes, outlined by lines of latitude and longitude, contain countries, or at least the mainland part where there are islands or detached portions. Your task is to decide which countries. (As a hint, all the countries on this page are found on Maps B, C and D of the Geography National Curriculum.) Write your answers in the centre of each box.

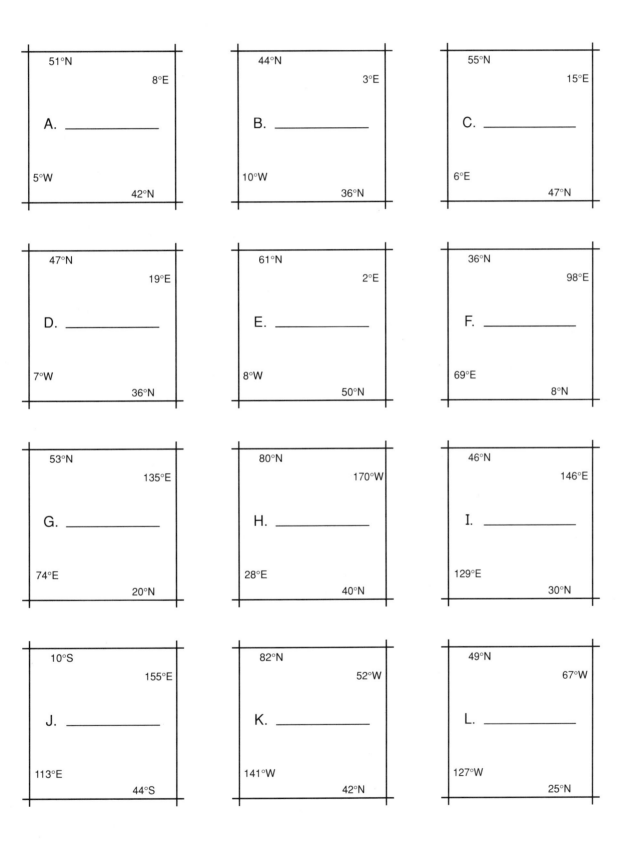

Box	North	East	West	South
A. ______	51°N	8°E	5°W	42°N
B. ______	44°N	3°E	10°W	36°N
C. ______	55°N	15°E	6°E	47°N
D. ______	47°N	19°E	7°W	36°N
E. ______	61°N	2°E	8°W	50°N
F. ______	36°N	98°E	69°E	8°N
G. ______	53°N	135°E	74°E	20°N
H. ______	80°N	170°W	28°E	40°N
I. ______	46°N	146°E	129°E	30°N
J. ______	10°S	155°E	113°E	44°S
K. ______	82°N	52°W	141°W	42°N
L. ______	49°N	67°W	127°W	25°N

Q57 - Where on earth ...? (2)

These boxes, outlined by lines of latitude and longitude, contain countries, or at least the mainland part where there are islands or detached portions. Your task is to decide which countries. (As a hint, all the countries on this page are found on Maps E and F of the Geography National Curriculum.) Write your answers in the centre of each box.

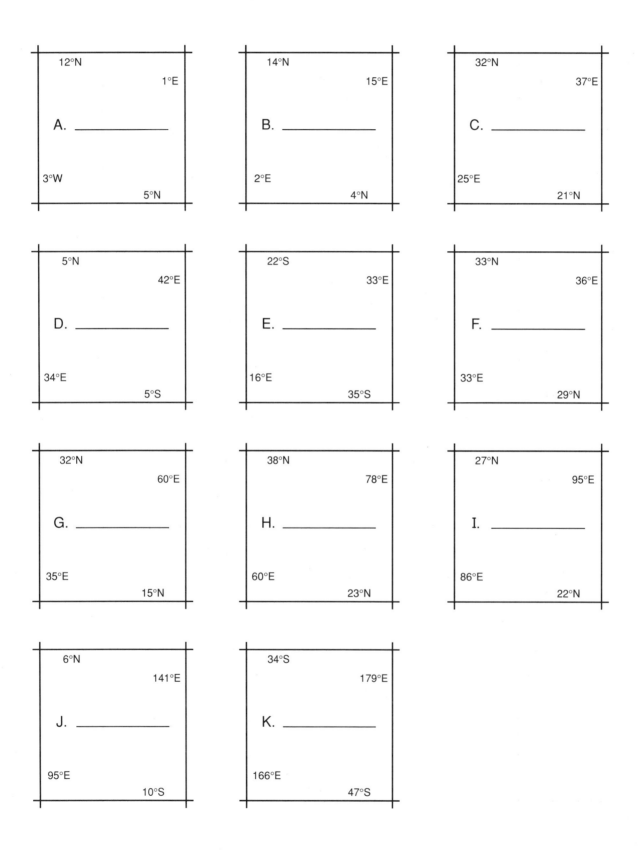

Box	North/South edge (top)	East edge	West edge	North/South edge (bottom)
A. ____________	12°N	1°E	3°W	5°N
B. ____________	14°N	15°E	2°E	4°N
C. ____________	32°N	37°E	25°E	21°N
D. ____________	5°N	42°E	34°E	5°S
E. ____________	22°S	33°E	16°E	35°S
F. ____________	33°N	36°E	33°E	29°N
G. ____________	32°N	60°E	35°E	15°N
H. ____________	38°N	78°E	60°E	23°N
I. ____________	27°N	95°E	86°E	22°N
J. ____________	6°N	141°E	95°E	10°S
K. ____________	34°S	179°E	166°E	47°S

Q58 - Where on earth ...? (3)

These boxes, outlined by lines of latitude and longitude, contain countries, or at least the mainland part where there are islands or detached portions. Your task is to decide which countries. (As a hint, all the countries on this page are found on Maps E and F of the Geography National Curriculum.) Write your answers in the centre of each box.

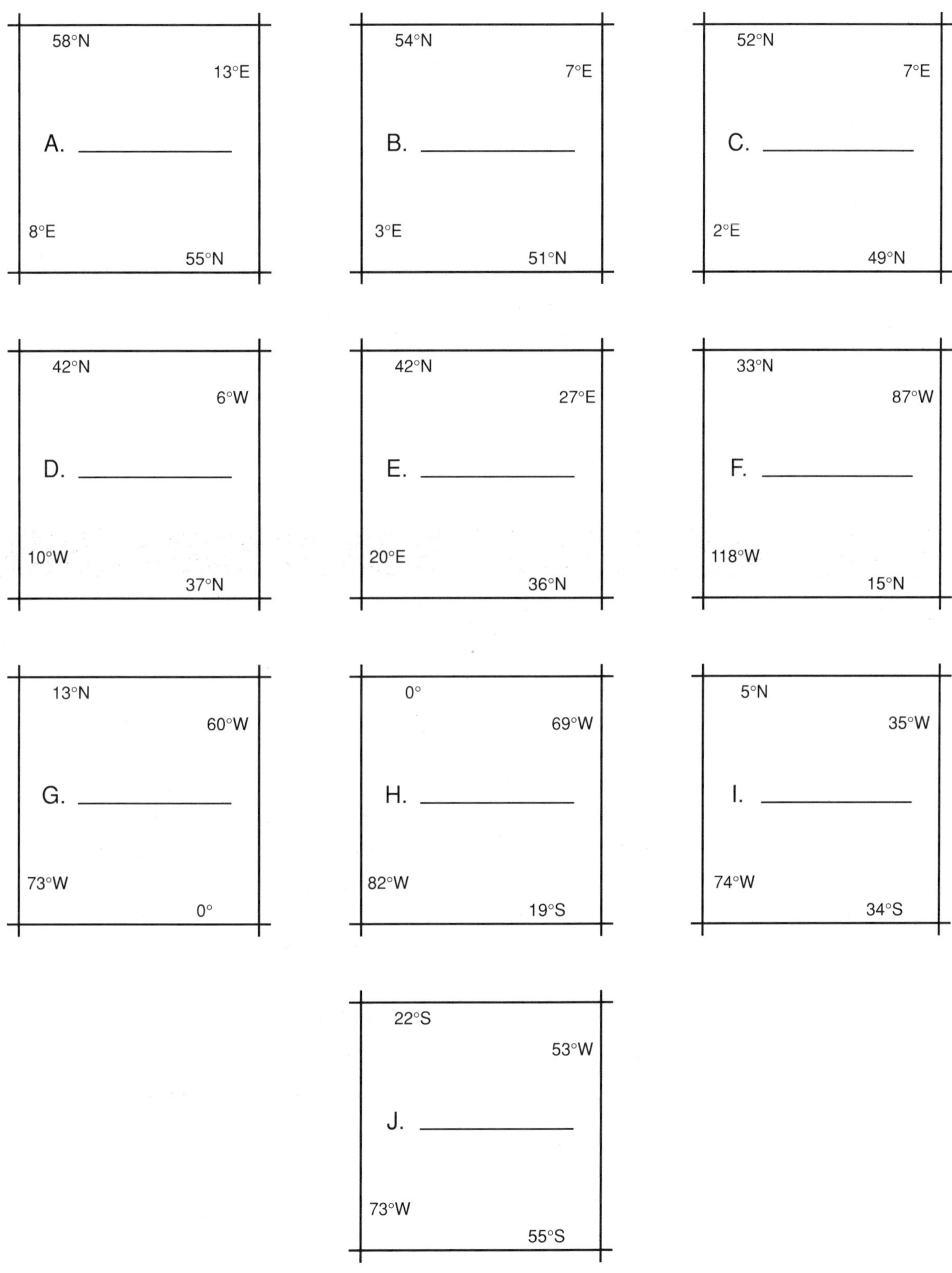

Q59 - British rivers (3)

Find and ring the listed river names. The remaining letters spell out the name of one river outside Britain.

Y	A	T	C	M	T	Y	N	E	I	T
T	H	A	M	E	S	S	I	S	I	R
A	M	W	E	Y	D	E	E	W	T	A
M	S	S	D	W	E	L	L	A	N	D
A	S	O	W	E	N	X	V	L	E	A
R	N	Y	A	R	E	O	E	E	D	M
I	I	W	Y	T	N	O	V	A	E	S
C	H	E	R	W	E	L	L	R	R	S
L	A	F	L	H	T	S	S	I	I	S
Y	A	U	T	T	T	E	R	R	A	P
D	N	R	P	O	Y	I	M	E	P	E
E	O	O	U	S	E	I	N	E	S	Y
F	T	R	E	N	T	E	N	N	E	K

AIRE
ARUN
AVON (x 2)
CAM
CHERWELL
CLYDE
DART
DEE (x2)
DON
EDEN
ESK
EXE
FAL
FORTH
ISIS
KENNET
LEA
LUNE
MEDWAY
MERSEY
NENE
NITH
OUSE
PARRETT
SPEY
STOUR
SWALE
TAMAR
TAW
TAY
TEES
TEME
THAMES
TRENT
TWEED
TYNE
TYWI
WELLAND
WEY
WYE
YARE

Write your answer here.

1__________________

Q60 - European countries (3)

Find and ring the names of the listed countries. The remaining letters spell out the names of five European capital cities.

S	W	I	T	Z	E	R	L	A	N	D	S	L	E	S	S
P	S	U	A	O	R	E	B	D	E	N	M	A	R	K	A
A	I	A	S	I	C	G	R	A	D	A	V	E	H	N	I
I	L	R	N	E	R	A	H	B	E	L	G	I	U	M	V
N	F	B	E	M	Y	A	N	P	W	N	E	A	N	A	A
N	A	R	A	L	A	G	G	O	S	I	R	I	G	I	L
O	G	E	A	N	A	R	B	L	M	F	M	R	A	N	S
R	E	T	R	N	I	N	I	A	U	N	A	T	R	A	O
W	I	M	L	O	C	A	D	N	H	B	N	S	Y	M	G
A	K	C	O	T	S	E	B	D	O	U	Y	U	C	U	U
Y	U	R	P	O	R	T	U	G	A	L	E	A	S	R	Y
T	I	A	I	K	A	V	O	L	S	O	H	C	E	Z	C

ALBANIA
AUSTRIA
BELGIUM
BULGARIA
CZECHOSLOVAKIA
DENMARK
FINLAND
FRANCE
GERMANY
GREECE
HUNGARY
IRELAND
ITALY
MONACO
NORWAY
POLAND
PORTUGAL
RUMANIA
SAN MARINO
SPAIN
SWEDEN
SWITZERLAND
YUGOSLAVIA

Write your answers here.

1____________ 4____________

2____________ 5____________

3____________

Q61 - Asian capitals

Find and ring the listed names of capital cities and one former capital.
The remaining letters spell out the names of seven island groups around Asia.

K	H	U	L	A	N	B	A	T	O	R	A	N	D	A	K
O	U	O	O	B	M	O	L	O	C	M	D	N	J	N	U
K	D	A	C	C	A	N	I	C	O	B	A	O	A	E	A	W
G	R	R	L	H	N	R	Y	U	K	K	D	O	K	N	G	A
N	Y	U	T	A	I	P	E	I	A	A	H	G	A	A	N	I
A	K	U	M	Y	L	M	R	V	B	I	G	N	R	I	A	T
B	L	M	A	U	A	U	I	A	U	M	A	A	T	T	Y	A
L	A	D	O	R	D	C	M	N	L	R	B	R	A	N	G	I
I	H	E	A	V	T	A	E	P	H	N	O	M	P	E	N	H
S	S	K	E	O	L	Y	C	E	U	C	H	E	L	I	O	L
L	N	E	R	S	S	M	T	T	U	R	I	E	B	V	Y	E
A	A	I	I	U	R	I	U	D	N	A	M	T	A	K	P	D
D	A	M	A	S	C	U	S	T	I	T	O	K	Y	O	U	S

AMMAN
ANKARA
BAGHDAD
BANGKOK
BEIRUT
COLOMBO
DACCA
DAMASCUS
DELHI
DJAKARTA
HO CHI MINH CITY
ISLAMABAD
KABUL
KATMANDU
KUALA LUMPUR
KUWAIT
MANILA
PHNOM PENH
PYONGYANG
RANGOON
RIYADH
SEOUL
TAIPEI
TEHRAN
TOKYO
ULAN BATOR
VICTORIA
VIENTIANE

Write your answers here.

1 ____________ 5 ____________

2 ____________ 6 ____________

3 ____________ 7 ____________

4 ____________

Q62 - Asian countries (3)

Find and ring the listed names of Asian countries.
The remaining letters spell out the names of four other countries of the region.

M	O	N	G	S	Y	R	I	A	O	T	A	L	I
T	U	S	S	R	E	C	H	I	N	A	I	A	M
H	A	L	A	I	K	I	Y	S	A	I	D	N	I
A	S	I	R	L	R	N	L	R	D	W	O	A	M
I	X	A	S	A	U	D	I	A	R	A	B	I	A
L	Q	P	N	N	T	O	H	E	O	N	M	I	N
A	E	R	O	K	L	N	I	L	J	S	A	N	T
N	N	O	N	A	B	E	L	P	P	I	C	A	E
D	N	E	N	A	T	S	I	K	A	P	S	P	I
Q	A	N	A	T	S	I	N	A	H	G	F	A	V
T	B	A	N	G	L	A	D	E	S	H	A	J	R

AFGHANISTAN
BANGLADESH
CAMBODIA
CHINA
INDIA
INDONESIA
IRAN
IRAQ
ISRAEL
JAPAN
JORDAN
KOREA
LAOS
LEBANON
PAKISTAN
SAUDI ARABIA
SRI LANKA
SYRIA
TAIWAN
THAILAND
TURKEY
USSR
VIETNAM

Write your answers here.

1 ____________ 3 ____________

2 ____________ 4 ____________

Q63 - American countries (2)

Find and ring the listed names of American countries.
The remaining letters spell out the names of five of their capital cities.

T H O N D U R A S E G A U C C

I A C I R A T S O C R U Y O G

A M L E C A P A S B O G A L A

N E P J G H L O S E D A U O A

E X A S U M I E A L A R G M L

Y I N N Y A Z L U I U A A B A

A C A N A D A G E Z C C R I M

U O M A N I R U S E E I A A E

G U A A A B B U E N O N P S T

U A I R O D A V L A S L E R A

R A R G E N T I N A E S C V U

U A R A C A S A I V I L O B G

ARGENTINA
BELIZE
BOLIVIA
BRAZIL
CANADA
CHILE
COLOMBIA
COSTA RICA
ECUADOR
EL SALVADOR
GUATEMALA
GUYANA
HONDURAS
MEXICO
NICARAGUA
PANAMA
PARAGUAY
PERU
SURINAM
URUGUAY
USA
VENEZUELA

Write your answers here.

1__________ 4__________

2__________ 5__________

3__________

Q64 - American capitals (2)

Find and ring the listed names of capital cities.
The remaining letters spell out the names of four islands near South America.

M O N T E V I D E O J U A N F

E R W N A P L A G I C U G E T

A N O M D E B O G O T A Z F A

L G T A K L R T C A Y E N N E

B U E N O S A I R E S S A A A

S A G A C A S U N C I O N M N

A T R G I N I Q N D A J A S O

C E O U X T L O U W T N V H T

A M E A E I I A A G A A A E S

R A G O M A A T P P R S H G G

A L I A A G T S O A U T H S N

C A N A P O M L E B Z A N D I

W I C H O B I R A M A R A P K

ASUNCION
BELMOPAN
BOGOTA
BRASILIA
BUENOS AIRES
CARACAS
CAYENNE
GEORGETOWN
GUATEMALA
HAVANA
KINGSTON
LA PAZ
LIMA
MANAGUA
MEXICO
MONTEVIDEO
OTTAWA
PANAMA
PARAMARIBO
QUITO
SAN JOSE
SANTIAGO
TEGUCIGALPA

Write your answers here.

1__________ 3__________

2__________ 4__________

Q65 - States of the USA (2)

Find and ring the listed names of the US states. The remaining letters spell out six names of other states, a district and neighbouring countries.

N W Y O M I N G E R I H S P M A H W E N
A A W E S S A S N A K D N A L Y R A M T
G D A T O K A D L V K I S A X E T S T R
I I S G A I N A V L Y S N N E P I H U I
H R C N H E B N E V A D A I I N A I C A
C O A A W A A S E C O O A L D W U N I T
I L R Y M N T R H H M K M I A H E G T D
M F O A O I M U I I S A A I H K R T C O
O R L Z O O S O S A N N I T O O A O E D
K A I K N E E S R L A M N N E W W N N A
L R N T T T I B O U O R E G O N A C N R
A K A T Y S E D I U S U T X R I L C O O
H T S A S N A K R A R O I F I C E O C L
O L U I S I O N I L L I M S B C D I A O
M C P A A N A T N O M N A N I L O R A C
A P N A D A M A I N I G R I V A E X I C
I C A L I F O R N I A E E S S E N N E T
Y E S R E J W E N R H O D E I S L A N D
W I S C O N S I N O X A T O S E N N I M

ALABAMA
ALASKA
ARIZONA
ARKANSAS
CALIFORNIA
CAROLINA N.
COLORADO
CONNECTICUT
DAKOTA
DELAWARE
FLORIDA
GEORGIA
HAWAII
IDAHO
ILLINOIS
INDIANA

IOWA
KANSAS
LOUISIANA
MAINE
MARYLAND
MASSACHUSETTS
MICHIGAN
MINNESOTA
MISSISSIPPI
MISSOURI
MONTANA
NEBRASKA
NEVADA
NEW HAMPSHIRE
NEW JERSEY
NEW YORK

N. MEXICO
OHIO
OKLAHOMA
OREGON
PENNSYLVANIA
RHODE ISLAND
S. CAROLINA
TENNESSEE
TEXAS
UTAH
VERMONT
VIRGINIA
WASHINGTON
WISCONSIN
WYOMING

Write your answers here.

1 ____________________

2 ____________________

3 ____________________

4 ____________________

5 ____________________

6 ____________________

Q66 - Counties of England and Wales

Find and ring the named English counties.

The remaining letters spell out seven other counties and one former county.

B	U	C	K	I	N	G	H	A	M	H	U	R	E	T	S	E	C	I	E	L
M	E	D	I	S	Y	E	S	R	E	M	D	U	R	H	A	M	B	D	E	I
R	G	R	E	A	T	E	R	M	A	N	C	H	E	S	T	E	R	E	Y	S
S	I	D	E	T	Y	N	E	A	N	D	W	E	A	R	D	A	N	V	E	L
O	S	O	U	T	H	Y	O	R	K	S	H	I	R	E	R	S	T	O	R	E
N	N	C	T	C	U	M	B	R	I	A	I	N	G	C	O	T	H	N	R	O
O	A	A	M	N	S	T	A	W	T	F	F	C	L	O	F	S	R	I	U	F
R	D	M	G	O	N	N	O	B	A	H	O	W	R	T	T	U	H	H	S	W
T	A	B	R	R	L	M	S	D	E	R	Y	P	T	O	R	S	N	K	G	I
H	E	R	E	F	O	R	D	A	N	D	W	O	R	C	E	S	T	E	R	G
U	R	I	A	O	C	M	N	W	L	A	F	I	R	H	H	E	O	N	T	H
M	I	D	T	L	N	U	A	V	O	N	L	O	C	K	C	X	E	T	N	T
B	H	G	E	K	I	L	L	L	S	D	B	E	R	K	S	H	I	R	E	T
E	S	E	R	D	L	X	D	T	G	S	E	E	V	D	P	H	R	W	W	E
R	P	T	L	D	E	E	I	S	T	U	S	R	U	E	S	O	I	S	G	S
L	O	E	O	E	E	S	M	D	E	F	Y	D	B	X	L	W	W	R	I	R
A	R	S	N	N	L	S	T	O	X	F	O	R	D	Y	T	C	S	Y	E	E
N	H	R	D	Y	W	E	S	T	Y	O	R	K	S	H	I	R	E	H	S	M
D	S	O	O	W	I	R	E	E	R	L	A	N	C	A	S	H	I	R	E	O
U	T	D	N	G	L	A	W	N	D	K	E	R	I	H	S	P	M	A	H	S

AVON
BEDFORD
BERKSHIRE
BUCKINGHAM
CAMBRIDGE
CHESHIRE
CLEVELAND
CLWYD
CORNWALL
CUMBRIA
DERBY
DEVON
DORSET
DURHAM
DYFED

EAST SUSSEX
ESSEX
GLAMORGAN
GREATER LONDON
GREATER MANCHESTER
GWENT
GWYNEDD
HAMPSHIRE
HEREFORD AND WORCESTER
HERTFORD
ISLE OF WIGHT
KENT
LANCASHIRE
LEICESTER
LINCOLN

MERSEYSIDE
NORFOLK
NORTHUMBERLAND
NORTH YORKSHIRE
OXFORD
POWYS
SHROPSHIRE
SOMERSET
SOUTH YORKSHIRE
SUFFOLK
SURREY
TYNE AND WEAR
WARWICK
WEST MIDLANDS
WEST YORKSHIRE

Write your answers here.

1 ____________________

2 ____________________

3 ____________________

4 ____________________

5 ____________________

6 ____________________

7 ____________________

8 ____________________

Which one is the former county ?

____

Q67 - Great lakes of the world (2)

Find and ring the listed names. The remaining letters spell out three other lakes.

A	D	R	A	G	G	R	E	A	T	B	E	A	R
T	N	W	T	P	T	U	R	K	A	N	A	N	P
H	A	I	R	O	T	C	I	V	O	E	R	I	E
A	G	N	N	O	N	Y	A	N	Y	E	G	H	T
B	I	N	E	P	U	L	G	R	N	R	T	M	I
A	H	I	A	O	G	R	E	A	T	S	A	L	T
S	C	P	G	E	N	A	V	S	T	L	N	B	I
C	I	E	H	I	T	T	T	E	A	R	A	N	C
A	M	G	E	N	E	V	A	W	L	P	I	H	A
V	L	A	K	Y	A	B	I	R	C	A	A	A	C
O	S	U	P	E	R	I	O	R	I	D	R	R	A
L	N	O	G	I	P	I	N	A	G	O	D	A	L
T	A	G	U	E	V	A	L	S	T	A	E	R	G
A	B	O	T	I	N	A	M	H	U	R	O	N	A

ARAL
ATHABASCA
BAYKAL
CHAD
ERIE
EYRE
GARDA
GENEVA
GREAT BEAR
GREAT SALT
GREAT SLAVE
HURON
LADOGA
MALAWI
MANITOBA
MICHIGAN
NEAGH
NIPIGON
ONTARIO
POOPO
SUPERIOR
TANA
TITICACA
TONLE SAP
TURKANA
VANERN
VICTORIA
VOLTA
WINNIPEG

Write your answers here.

1 ____________ 3 ____________

2 ____________

Q68 - The weather station (2)

Find and ring the listed words. The remaining letters spell out six words connected with wind.

C	A	E	R	U	T	A	R	E	P	M	E	T	M	D	L
L	S	D	E	W	G	M	A	B	L	I	Z	Z	A	R	D
L	B	T	T	R	A	E	B	F	E	L	V	Z	X	Y	E
A	O	B	E	A	U	F	O	R	T	I	A	G	I	B	E
F	N	H	M	V	G	R	S	O	A	A	N	T	M	U	R
N	L	E	O	I	E	O	I	S	O	H	E	L	U	L	U
I	E	C	R	C	S	N	Y	T	I	Y	E	R	M	B	S
A	A	W	A	O	L	T	S	F	H	X	A	I	U	S	S
R	R	O	B	L	I	A	T	O	O	I	S	M	M	R	E
W	T	N	M	D	M	D	S	G	N	H	U	E	I	R	R
E	H	S	I	F	R	I	S	U	N	S	H	I	N	E	P
A	I	M	E	R	C	U	R	Y	C	A	C	W	I	N	D
T	U	C	L	O	U	D	C	O	V	E	R	R	M	N	E
H	B	E	A	N	E	M	O	M	E	T	E	R	E	A	U
E	F	W	E	T	B	U	L	B	O	R	T	S	C	E	A
R	L	E	P	R	E	C	I	P	I	T	A	T	I	O	N

ALCOHOL
ANEMOMETER
ANEROID
BAROMETER
BEAUFORT
BLIZZARD
CALM
CLOUD COVER
COLD FRONT
DEW
DRYBULB
EARTH
FOG
FRONT
FROST
GAUGE
HAIL
HUMIDITY
ISOBAR
ISOHEL
ISOHYET
MAXIMUM
MERCURY
MINIMUM
MIST
PRECIPITATION
PRESSURE
RAIN
RAINFALL
RIME
SIXS
SNOW
STEVENSON SCREEN
SUNSHINE
TEMPERATURE
VANE
WEATHER
WET BULB
WIND

Write your answers here.

1 ____________ 4 ____________

2 ____________ 5 ____________

3 ____________ 6 ____________

Q69 - Energy

Wind is a renewable energy resource; windmills are coming back into fashion as sources of power. In this puzzle all the answers have to do with energy and power. Each word starts from the central circle of the windmill, works outwards and is numbered at the end.

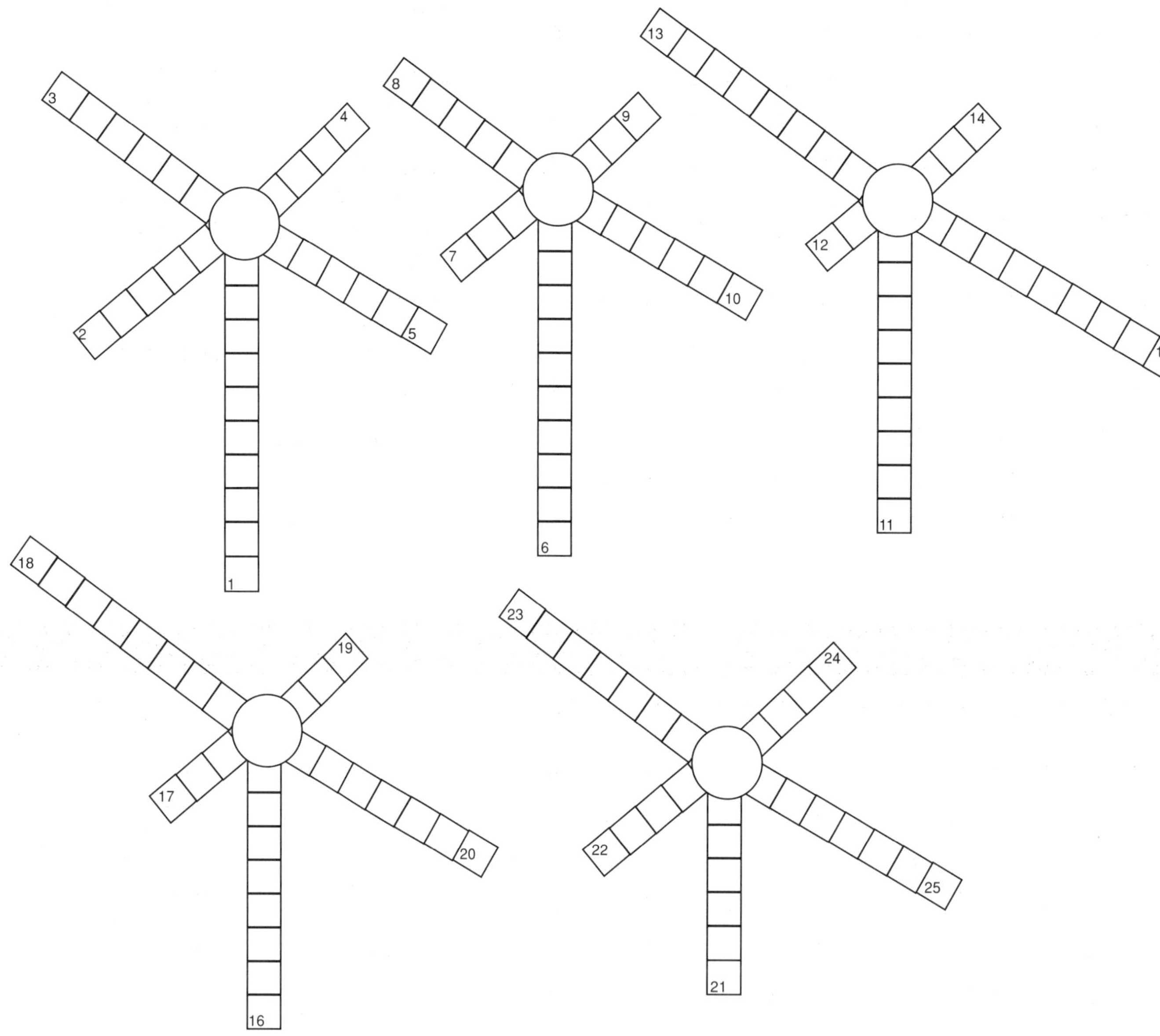

1 Changes current from one level to another
2 Carries oil around the world
3 Electricity generated by heat
4 Ups & downs of the sea
5 Spun round by water in an HEP station
6 Reactor producing more fuel than it uses
7 Petrol & diesel are two examples of this
8 Putting atoms together to produce energy
9 Probably the original source of heat
10 Goes on in a nuclear reactor
11 Heat from the earth
12 From the North Sea to your cooker
13 Produces electricity
14 Distributes electricity round the country
15 Effect when the world gets too hot
16 Used by Salter's ducks
17 Measure of electric power
18 Uses streams to grind corn
19 Probably the original 7
20 Once used for corn, now generating electricity
21 Short for synthetic fuels
22 Drives 5s in 3-power stations
23 Extracted at Kilve & Leith before petroleum was widely availab
24 From the sun
25 The ultimate source of heat, light and energy

Q70 - Settlements

If Christaller is to be believed, a hexagonal pattern can be found when studying settlements. This puzzle works with hexagons, each side of 6 letters but with words going in almost any direction as shown by arrows.

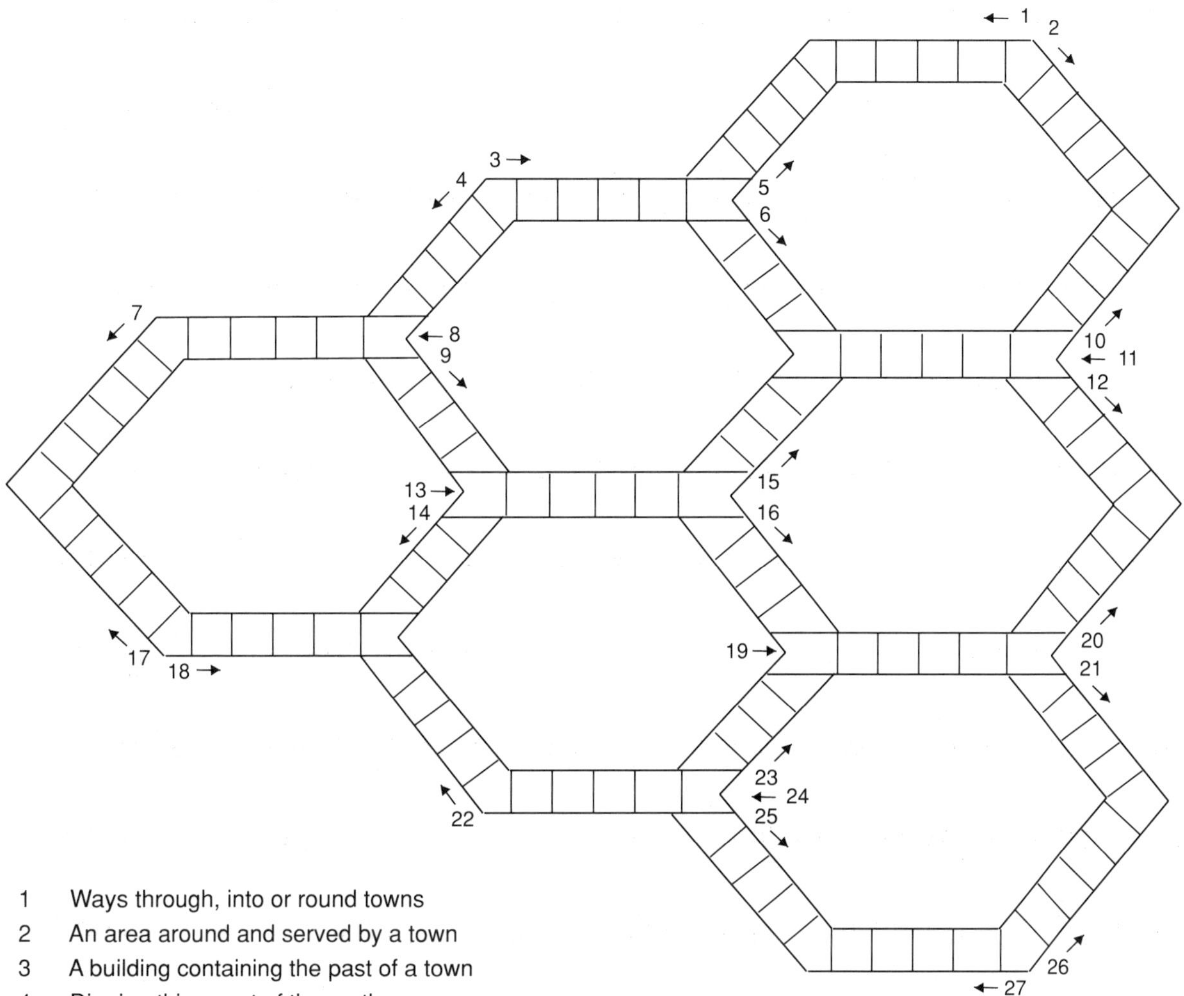

1 Ways through, into or round towns
2 An area around and served by a town
3 A building containing the past of a town
4 Digging things out of the earth
5 Burgess and Hoyt devised these of towns
6 Where goods are bought and sold - often the original function of a town
7 One of many found in the CBD
8 Racially segregated area - originally for Jews
9 Increase in size
10 Development along main road
11 Seaside town for holidays
12 Selling to the public
13 Most of the town is made up of these
14 Very small settlement without even a church
15 Most of 13 are found on one of these
16 Geometrical area at the centre of some towns
17 River crossing where a settlement might have grown
18 'Disease' affecting run-down area of town
19 Suburban areas detached from and outside town
20 Related to characteristics like class or standard of living
21 Pedestrian underpass in UK, tube railway in USA
22 Incentive offered to get movement
23 Without these a town would be empty
24 Open to all - building, house or space
25 A small area of land - sent by post?
26 Informal building housing arrivals in Third World city
27 Place of education

Q71 - Cops and robbers

All of the symbols shown here appear on 1:50 000-scale Ordnance Survey maps. Each symbol is numbered. Write the meaning of the symbols in the numbered space provided below.

Two robbers stole a car from a 1  red and robbed a bank, taking a customer, John Green, as hostage. They made their getaway along a 2  A213 red until it went into a 3  where they turned off along a 4  B4567 brown over a 5  then down a 6 >> . At the bottom they tied up John and left him in a 7 **PC**. They didn't do a very good job as John freed himself, found a 8  and called the police. As he was beside a 9 **MS** the police knew where to find him.

Meanwhile the robbers had been delayed at a 10 **LC** and then the road ran along an 11  which made them easy to spot. They needed a place like a 12 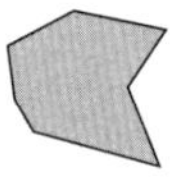 green to hide in, but there wasn't one, not even an 13 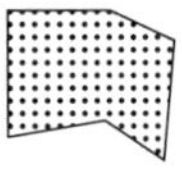 green. The only place to hide was a 14  so they turned off at the 15  and drove up to it. The first thing they saw from the 16  blue beside it was a police car. Where could they go? The 17  had no way out, the car would get stuck on the 18  . There was only the small 19  FC green but before they reached it the car hit a 20  blue. The crooks jumped out of the car, ran off downhill, under a 21  past the 22 **PH**, in one door of the 23  and out of the other, they leapt over a wall and dodged through some 24  along a 25  red under the 26  and disappeared into one end of a 27  . At the other end the police, who had cut across the 28 , were waiting near a 29 red to arrest them.

1 __________	9 __________	17 __________	25 __________
2 __________	10 __________	18 __________	26 __________
3 __________	11 __________	19 __________	27 __________
4 __________	12 __________	20 __________	28 __________
5 __________	13 __________	21 __________	29 __________
6 __________	14 __________	22 __________	
7 __________	15 __________	23 __________	
8 __________	16 __________	24 __________	

Q72 - Our town

All the symbols shown here appear on 1:50 000-scale Ordnance Survey maps. Each symbol is numbered. Write the meaning of the symbols in the numbered space provided below.

You will like our town. It is full of interest as the [1]**Mus** shows. In 1066; the Saxons left a [2] on the outskirts, while the [3]**Cas** and [4]**Cath** in the centre are our best historic monuments. In the Victorian era some very odd buildings were put up, including the [5] **TH** and [6] red. The town started at the [7]  where the [8] red crosses the [9]  blue. There are lots of traffic jams today, even though there is a [10]  M69 blue around the town to the west. There was a fuss when it was built as the original route was through a [11]  grey, fortunately it was diverted. After all the area is a [12]  blue and part of it is a [13]  which may have had something to do with the decision.

The ugliest area of our town is the [14] 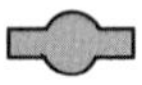 red which was developed in the 1960s. It is all grey concrete. If you like old buildings though we have several [15], one [16] has good [17]  blue from the top and there is a [18] blue up there too! I ought to warn you that there are too many [19]**PH**s and only two [20]**PC**s, and [21] P blue is not easy on Thursdays and Saturdays.

1 ____________
2 ____________
3 ____________
4 ____________
5 ____________
6 ____________
7 ____________
8 ____________
9 ____________
10 ____________
11 ____________
12 ____________
13 ____________
14 ____________
15 ____________
16 ____________
17 ____________
18 ____________
19 ____________
20 ____________
21 ____________

Q73 - A railway journey

All the symbols shown here appear on 1:50 000-scale Ordnance Survey maps. Each symbol is numbered. Write the meaning of the symbols in the numbered space provided below.

I like trains, especially for long journeys. We have a really big [1] red in our town, just down from the [2] **Cath**. It looks more spectacular than the [3] **TH**, which is a Victorian monstrosity!

If you go north on the train it dives into a [4] for three minutes then out along an [5] where you can see lots of [6] of factories. There are two [7] just before you leave the town and the line goes through a [8]. After that it first goes under a [9] and then, as the land drops away, over a [10] where you look down a valley. In the distance you can see a [11] appear among the [12] green. Soon the farmland gets richer and there are many [13] green and some large [14]. In the past the railway used to carry a lot of the produce from the country to the towns and because the land is flat here few [15] were built but many [16] **LC** had to be made.

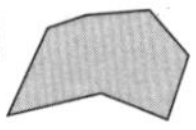

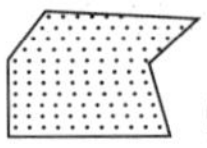

The next large town is more gloomy because the line goes through the middle of a [17] **Cemy**, then past [18] with abandoned trucks on them. Here the [19] red looks run down and the [20] red on the other side of the line has been covered with graffiti.

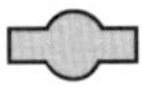

1 ______	6 ______	11 ______	16 ______
2 ______	7 ______	12 ______	17 ______
3 ______	8 ______	13 ______	18 ______
4 ______	9 ______	14 ______	19 ______
5 ______	10 ______	15 ______	20 ______

Q74 - Our holiday

All of the symbols shown here appear on 1:50 000-scale Ordnance Survey maps. Each symbol is numbered. Write the meaning of the symbols in the numbered space provided below.

When we went on holiday Mum and Dad insisted we stay at a [1]  blue, but I wanted to go to a [2] blue and my brother wanted to visit a [3] red with his friends. Mum and Dad said it was a nice place. There were [4] 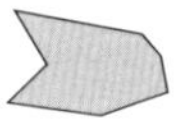 green to explore, a [5]  blue to play in, good [6]  from the [7] red nearby and a [8] 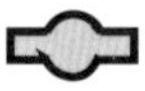 red in the town. It was close to several [9] red and [10] NT red properties.

The [11]  yellow was also quite close - actually it was down some steep [12]  . Most of the beach was either [13] 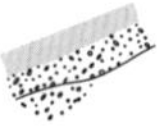 or [14]  and the water was warm. My brother got swept out to sea so we found a [15]  and contacted the [16]**CG Sta** who got on to the [17]**LB Sta** to rescue him. They had help from the RAF who landed at a[18] H nearby.

After that we stayed on dry land. We went to see [19]  s, a [20]**Cath**, and several [21]**Mus**. One day I got really bored, Dad went off to the [22]**PH** and Mum couldn't find any [23] P blue when I needed the [24]**PC**. Then we heard that Gran was ill so Dad rushed off along [25] M39 blue in the car. In fact Gran was in the [26]**Hosp** because she had fallen on the steps of a [27]  over a [28] A456 red. Dad came back that evening.

The next day Dad went to go to the [29] and spent a lot of time in the [30]**CH**. Meanwhile we bought stamps and postcards from the [31]**P** to send to our friends. From the [32] i blue we found out about some good [33] 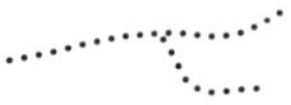 red and a local [34] 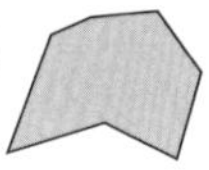 grey with a zoo. It was a good holiday after all !

1 ______	10 ______	19 ______	28 ______
2 ______	11 ______	20 ______	29 ______
3 ______	12 ______	21 ______	30 ______
4 ______	13 ______	22 ______	31 ______
5 ______	14 ______	23 ______	32 ______
6 ______	15 ______	24 ______	33 ______
7 ______	16 ______	25 ______	34 ______
8 ______	17 ______	26 ______	
9 ______	18 ______	27 ______	

Q75 - Gran's place

All of the symbols shown here appear on 1:50 000-scale Ordnance Survey maps. Each symbol is numbered. Write the meaning of the symbols in the numbered space provided below.

I really like visiting my Gran. We usually go by [1]  M29 blue getting on at [2] 2 blue and stop at a [3] S blue, before leaving at [4] 12 blue. Dad always says he hopes he won't need the [5]  blue. We leave the motorway, just after the [6]  and before the [7]  crosses it. First we turn along a [8]  brown which soon has a [9] >> up to the village. Then we go over a [10]  and turn off along the [11]  yellow - this is a difficult bit because of the sheep. You see, Gran lives in the middle of nowhere with a large [12] 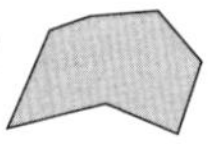 green behind her cottage. You can see a [13] blue on the top of the hill to the west. The village, according to the [14] **MS** is 5km away, and that only has a [15] **P** and a [16] + . Gran said there was a [17] **Sch** in the village when she was young. Now there are very few people living in the village. There used to be a [18] 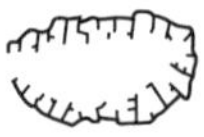 which closed shortly after Grandpa retired and lots of other people moved away. One of the larger houses is a [19] ▲ red for walkers - there are lots of [20] 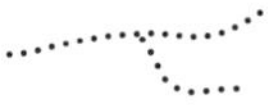 red around the village. One of them goes behind Gran's cottage and crosses the [21]  blue by a [22] . The authorities are thinking of putting a [23]  blue on Gran's side of the village. Gran says they will have to improve the [24] **P** blue in the village if they want to attract more visitors. In winter we leave when it is dark and the only lights to be seen are red ones on the [25]  15km away.

1 __________
2 __________
3 __________
4 __________
5 __________
6 __________
7 __________
8 __________
9 __________
10 __________
11 __________
12 __________
13 __________
14 __________
15 __________
16 __________
17 __________
18 __________
19 __________
20 __________
21 __________
22 __________
23 __________
24 __________
25 __________

A1 - Rivers (1)

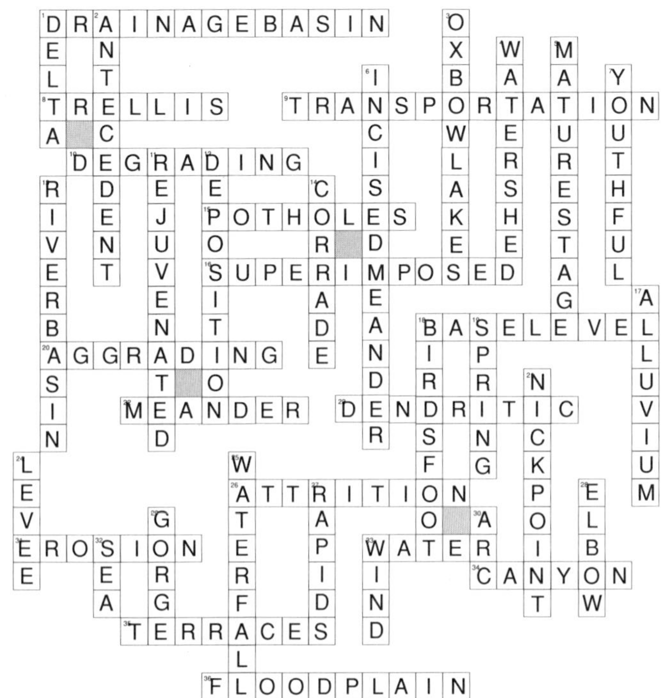

A2 - Volcanoes

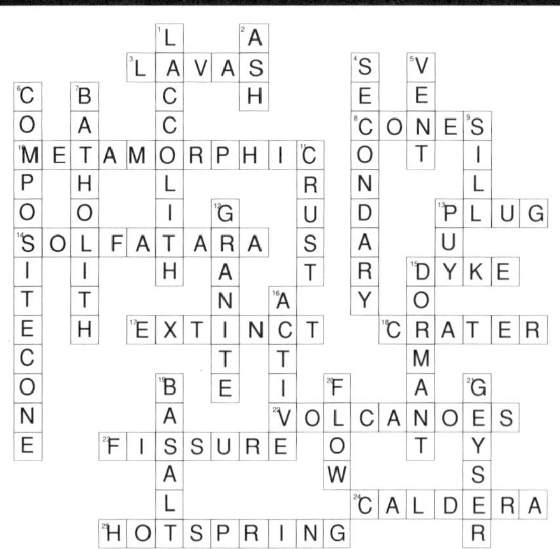

A3 - Plate tectonics

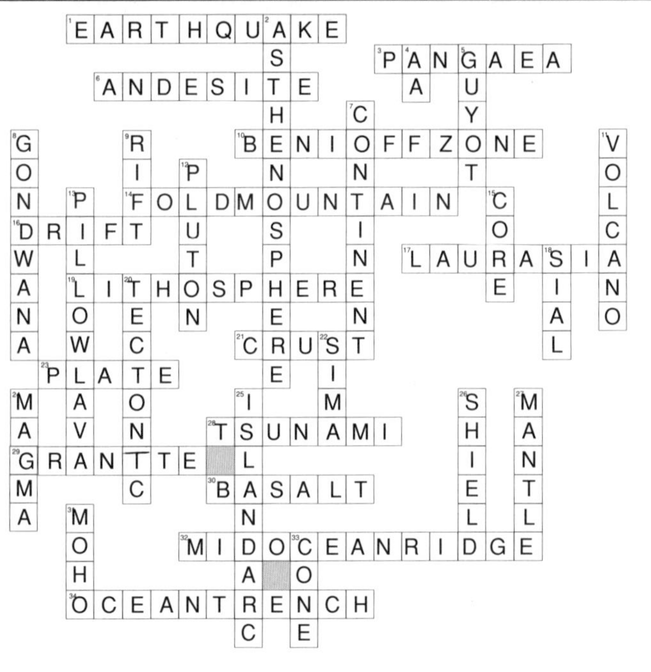

A4 - Clouds and rain (1)

A5 - Weather

A6 - Coasts (1)

A7 - Glaciers

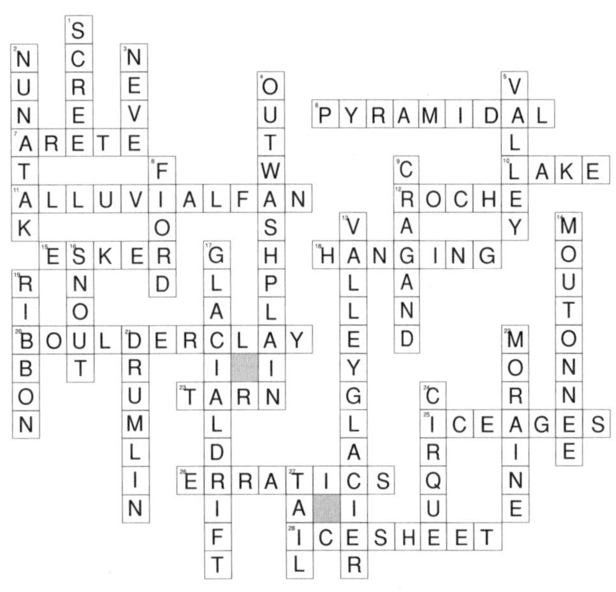

A8 - Limestone (1)

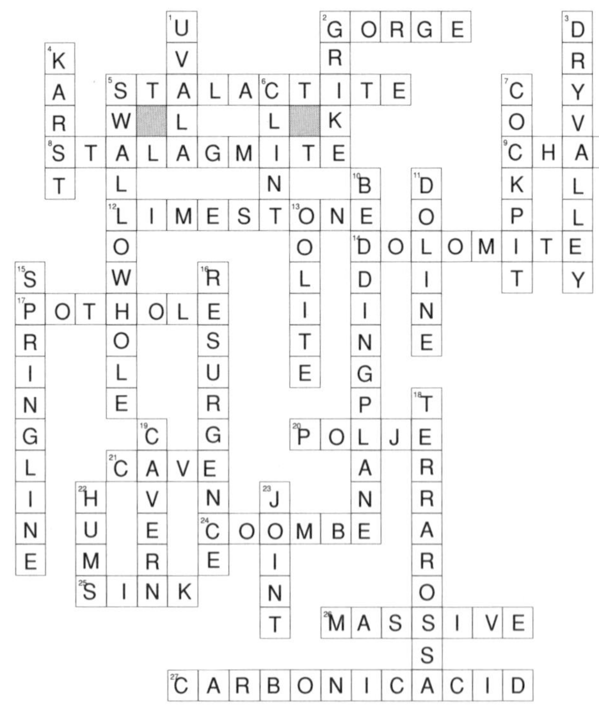

A9 - Rivers of the world

A10 - Mountain ranges

A11 - Seas and oceans

A12 - Mines and mining

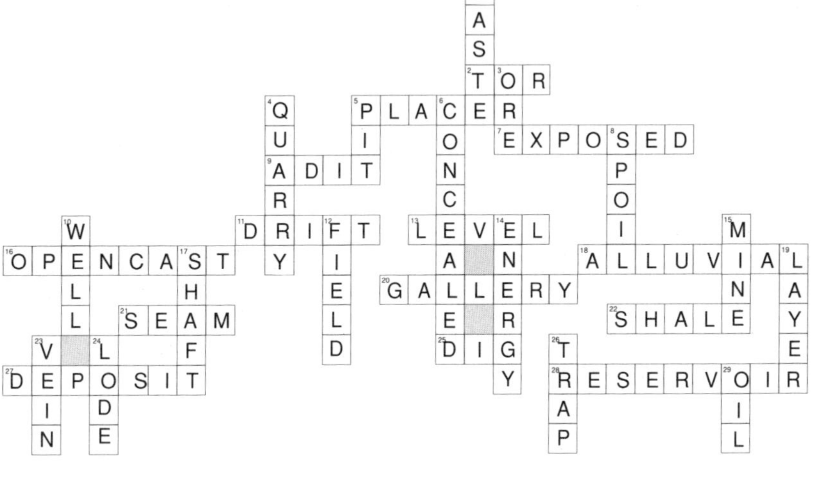

A13 - Identify these rivers

1 Isis 2 Severn 3 Tiber 4 Weser 5 Danube 6 Swanee 7 Seine 8 Thames 9 Loire 10 Nile
11 Ganges 12 Rhine 13 Don 14 Eden 15 Euphrates 16 Jordan 17 Somme 18 Orange
19 Amazon 20 Orinoco 21 Dee 22 Volga 23 Zambezi 24 Limpopo 25 Nelson

A14 - Words in words

1 Finland 2 Sweden 3 Bolivia 4 Spain 5 Oman 6 Rumania 7 Jamaica 8 Iceland 9 Portugal
10 Kuwait 11 Denmark 12 Ireland 13 Panama 14 Tonga 15 Singapore 16 Gibraltar
17 Paraguay 18 Thailand 19 Lebanon 20 Bahamas

A15 - Asian countries (1)

1 Korea 2 Thailand 3 Bangladesh 4 Malaysia 5 Indonesia 6 Vietnam 7 Philippines 8 Nepal
9 China 10 Cambodia

A16 - States of the USA (1)

1 Washington 2 Missouri 3 Pennsylvania 4 Virginia 5 Florida 6 Alabama 7 Kentucky 8 Nebraska
9 Minnesota 10 Montana 11 Oregon 12 California 13 Alaska 14 Mississippi 15 New Hampshire

A17 - Europe

1 English Channel 2 Atlantic 3 Mediterranean 4 Spain 5 Portugal 6 Pyrenees 7 Alps 8 Apennines
9 Po 10-11 Sicily, Sardinia 12 Corsica 13-14 Austria, Switzerland 15 Germany 16 Rhine
17 Netherlands 18 Denmark 19-20 Skaggerak, Kattegat 21-23 Norway, Sweden, Finland 24 Norway
25 Baltic 26 Bothnia 27 Greece 28 Danube

A18 - Asia

1 Russia 2 Arctic 3-5 Ob, Lena, Yenesei 6 China 7 Mongolia 8-13 Vietnam, Laos, Cambodia, Thailand, Burma, Malaysia 14-15 Irrawaddy, Mekong 16 Indonesia 17-18 Nepal, Bhutan 19 Himalaya
20 Bangladesh 21 Ganges 22 Pakistan 23 Indus 24 Sri Lanka 25 Red 26 Iran 27 Caspian

A19 - Africa

1 Atlantic 2 Indian 3 Madagascar 4-5 Tanganyika, Nyasa 6 Victoria 7 Nile 8 Mediterranean
9 Egypt 10 Red 11 Sudan 12 Sahara 13 Niger 14 Nigeria 15 Zaire or Congo 16 Somalia
17 South Africa 18 Tunisia 19 Senegal

A20 - Scottish regions and Welsh counties

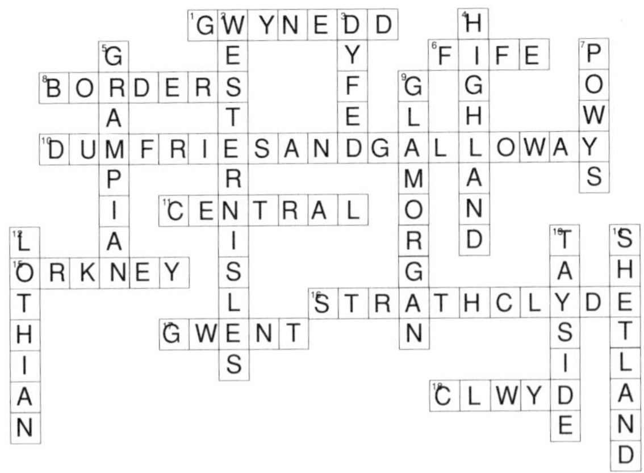

A21 - African countries

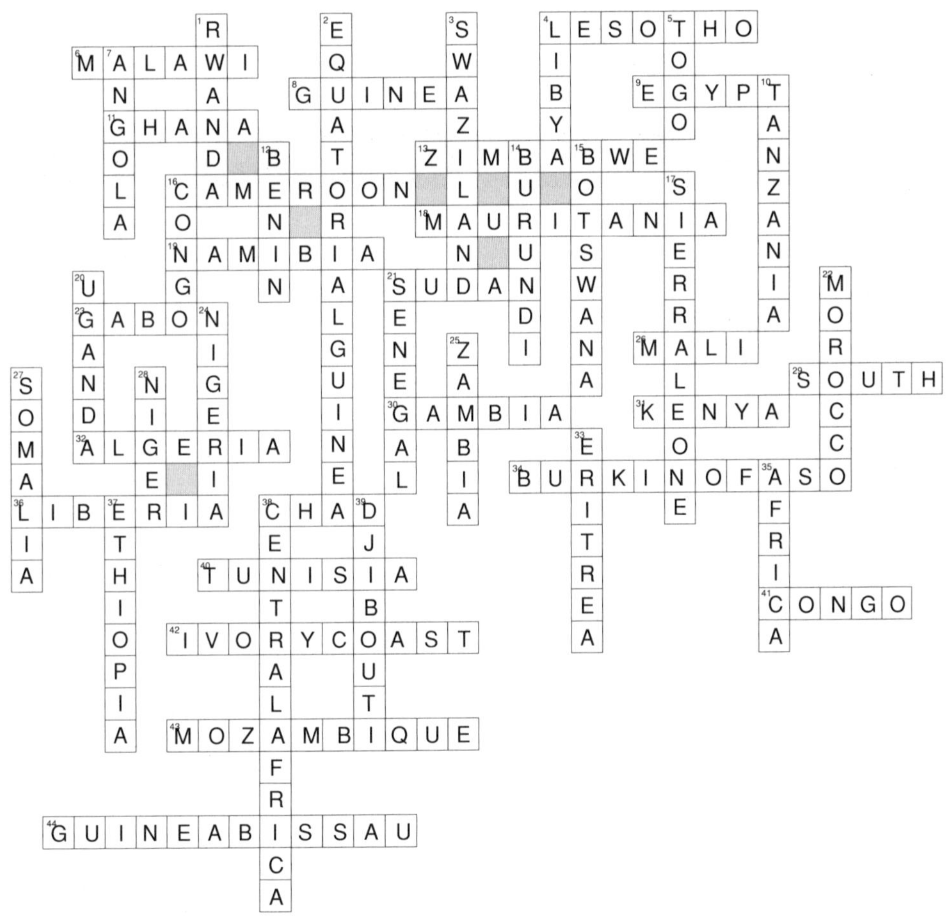

A22 - Asian countries (2) (1995)

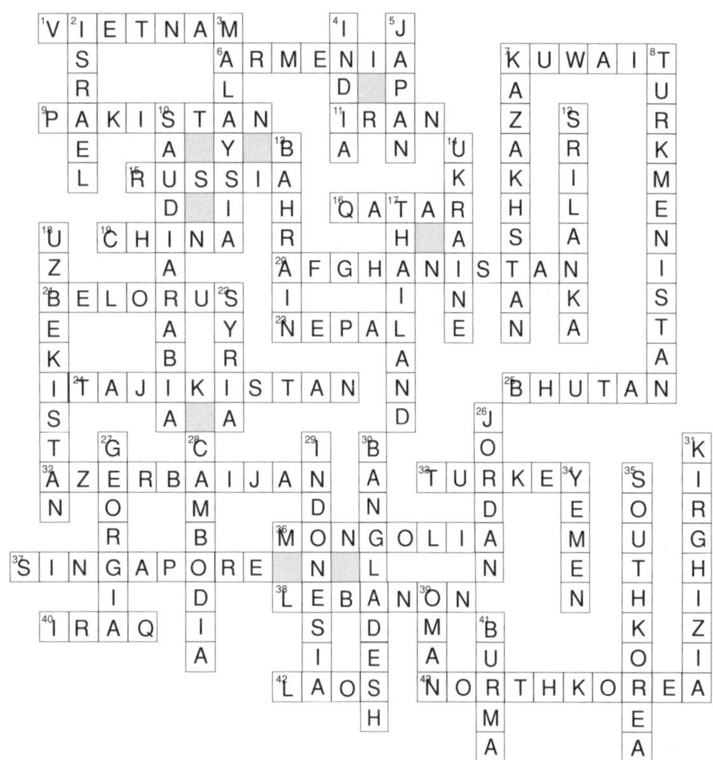

A23 - European countries (1) (1995)

A24 - American countries (1)

A25 - American capitals (1)

A26 - Great lakes of the world (1)

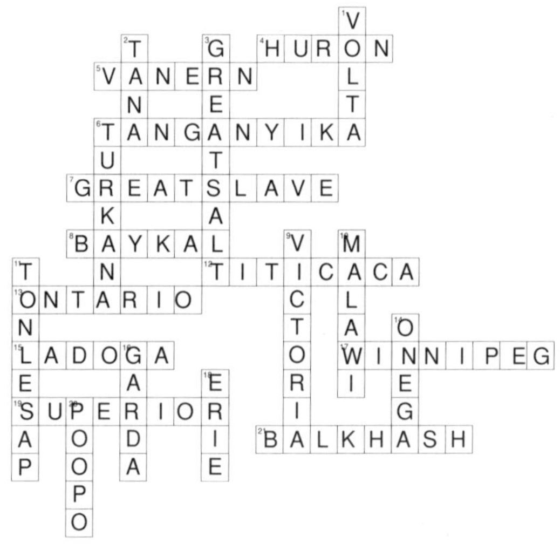

A27 - British rivers (1)

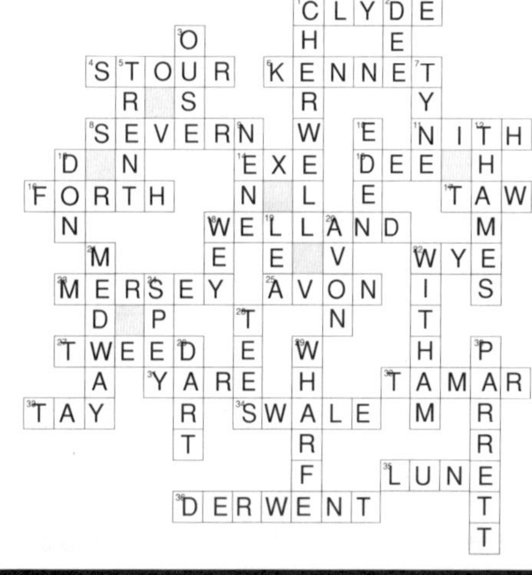

A28 - The weather station (1)

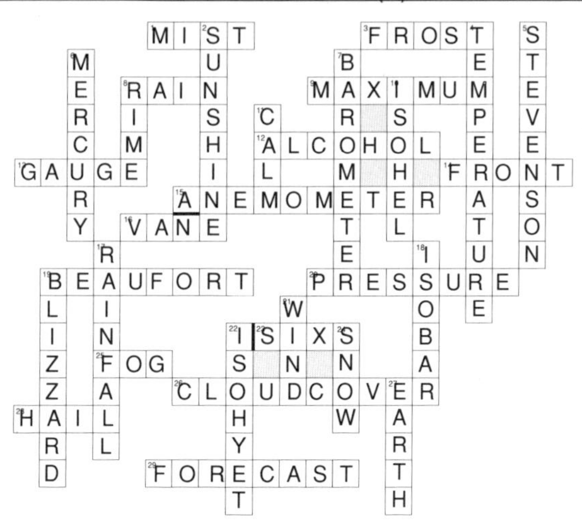

A29 - English counties

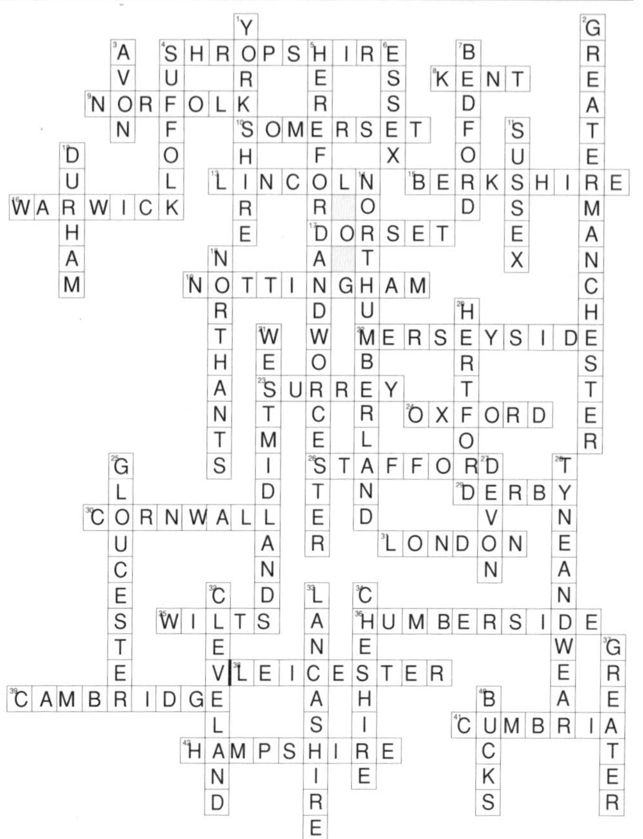

A30 - Capitals quiz

1 Rome 2 Copenhagen 3 Brussels 4 Khartoum 5 Santiago
6 Stockholm 7 Caracas 8 Baghdad 9 New Delhi
10 Quito, Libreville, Kampala 11 Kingston 12 Havana / Panama
13 Manila 14 Peking 15 Jerusalem 16 Damascus
17 Buenos Aires 18 Seoul 19 Athens 20 London, Accra
21 Paris 22 Budapest 23 Dublin 24 Vienna 25 Freetown
26 Monrovia 27 Cayenne 28 Wellington 29 Victoria
30 Vatican City

A31 - A town square

T	U	R	I	N	[2]G	H	E	T	T	[3]O	F
C	O	W	N	[9]S	L	U	[10]M	E	G	A	F
A	T	E	S	I	D	E	N	C	E	L	I
F	W	[14]R	A	N	S	P	O	R	[15]S	O	C
U	E	O	R	A	T	T	E	[20]T	H	P	E
N	[8]N	T	[19]T	U			[23]R	O	O	O	[4]S
A	O	C	L	Q	N		E	W	[16]P	L	H
[1]M	B	E	E	[22]S	O	I	G	[21]N	R	I	A
	B	[13]S	[18]B	U	E	L	C	U	I	[11]S	N
	I	S	R	U	X	[17]E	T	A	M	U	T
	[7]R	E	N	I	S	U	[12]B	R	U	B	I
	A	E	N	I	[6]L	A	I	C	O	[5]S	E

A32 - Missing vowels

1 India 2 Iran 3 Cuba 4 Peru 5 Iraq 6 Zaire 7 Mali
8 Togo 9 Italy 10 Chile 11 Congo 12 Benin 13 China
14 Sudan 15 Laos

A33 - Anagram countries (1)

1 Iran 2 Mali 3 Italy 4 Syria 5 Nepal 6 Cyprus
7 China 8 Spain 9 Lesotho 10 Denmark 11 Iceland
12 Peru 13 Malawi 14 Hungary 15 Sweden

A34 - Anagram countries (2)

1 Ghana 2 Brazil 3 Turkey 4 Poland 5 Taiwan
6 Uganda 7 Ecuador 8 Portugal 9 Ireland 10 Bolivia
11 Algeria 12 Monaco 13 Burma 14 Zaire 15 Pakistan

A35 - British rivers (2)

1 Thames 2 Wye 3 Severn 4 Don 5 Medway 6 Trent
7 Dee 8 Clyde 9 Tyne 10 Usk 11 Avon 12 Ouse

A36 - European countries (2)

1 Belgium 2 Luxembourg 3 Portugal 4 Albania 5 Austria
6 Hungary 7 Spain 8 Switzerland

A37 - South American countries (2)

1 Uruguay 2 Paraguay 3 Venezuela 4 Ecuador 5 Peru
6 Surinam 7 Colombia 8 Guyana 9 Bolivia 10 Chile
11 Argentina 12 Brazil

A38 - Tectonics

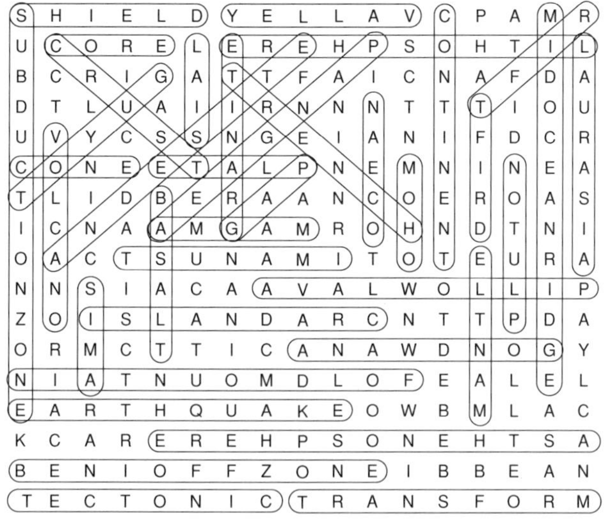

1 PACIFIC, 2 ATLANTIC, 3 INDIAN, 4 ARCTIC, 5 ANTARCTIC, 6 YELLOW, 7 BLACK, 8 CARIBBEAN

A39 - Volcanic activity

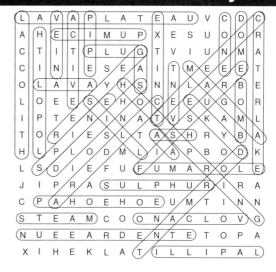

L A V A P L A T E A U V C D C
A H E C I M U P X E S U O O R
C T I T P L U G T V I U N M A
C I N I E S E A I T M E E E T
O L A V A Y H S N N L A R B E
L O E E S E H O C E E U G O R
I P T E N I N A T V S K A M L
T O R I E S L T A S H R Y B A
H L P L O D M L I A P B O D K
L S D I E F U F U M A R O L E
J I P R A S U L P H U R I R A
C P A H O E H O E U M T I N N
S T E A M C O O N A C L O V G
N U E E A R D E N T E T O P A
X I H E K L A T I L L I P A L

1 VESUVIUS, 2 ETNA, 3 STROMBOLI, 4 FUJI, 5 PARACUTIN, 6 COTOPAXI, 7 HEKLA

A40 - Folds and faults

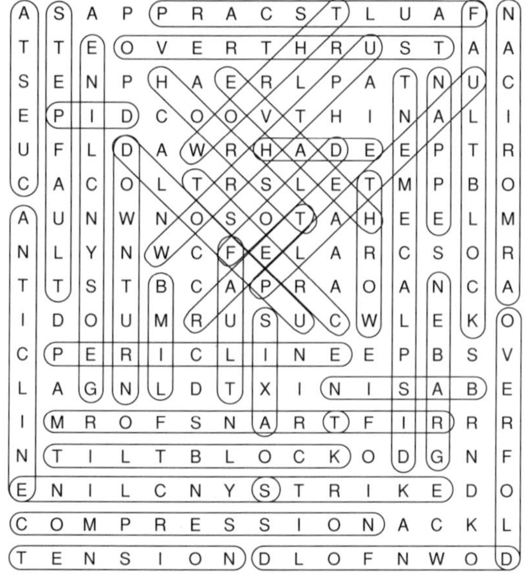

1 APPALACHIAN, 2 CASCADE, 3 ADIRONDACK

A41 - Soils

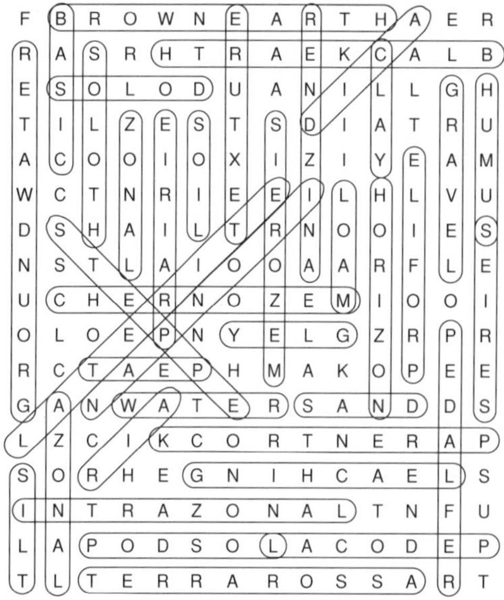

1 FERRALITIC, 2 SOLONCHAK, 3 CHESTNUT

A42 - Deserts

M U S H R O O M R O C K S E
D R A A A A L E H N A R N X
A N L M F S G O A A T M I F
P I I A I I B H E N U D A O
A L N D E S C M E S A T L L
A C A A S R A M M T S A P I
S W Q Y A O I N O R T A R A
I N U B A D L A N D S U E T
N R I R E S N E G U E Z B I
O G F P O Y A R D A N G B O
F D E F L A T I O N B I I N
A B R A S I O N M H O J G A
T V G D O O L F H S A L F E
B A J A D A N A I S E T R A

1 SAHARA, 2 NAMIB, 3 ATACAMA, 4 SONORAN, 5 GOBI, 6 MOJAVE

A43 - Glaciation

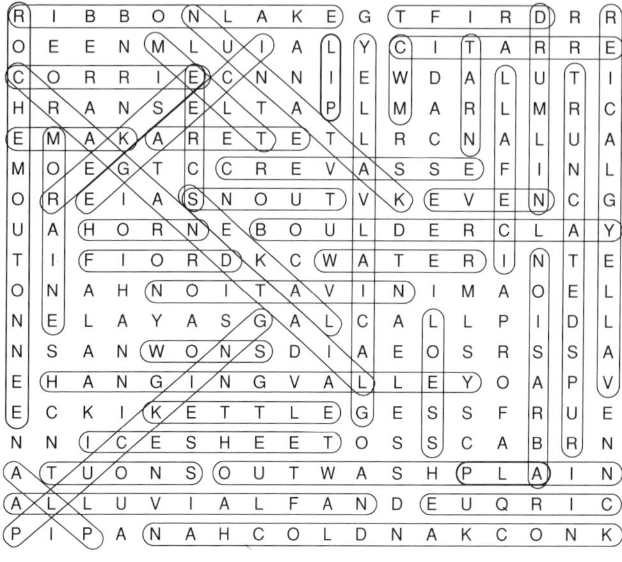

1 GREENLAND, 2 ANTARCTICA, 3 HIMALAYAS, 4 ALPS, 5 ANDES, 6 ROCKIES, 7 FENNOSCANDIA

A44 - Limestone (2)

C O C K P I T W S P R I N G S
A O O L I M E S T O N E O K I
R T C L I N T M A S S I V E N
B E D D I N G P L A N E E Y K
O R P N S T A L A C T I T E T
N R O R E S E P G I E M U H S
I A T E N E E K M P O L J E R
C R H V I G J O I N T D W A A
A O O A L R L E T R C H A L K
C S L C O O M B E L G L D A A
I S E N D G N I R P S C A V E
D A E C N E G R U S E R Y U R
S W A L L O W H O L E O G O F

1 WOOKEY, 2 SPEEDWELL, 3 DAN-YR-OGOF

A45 - Rivers (2)

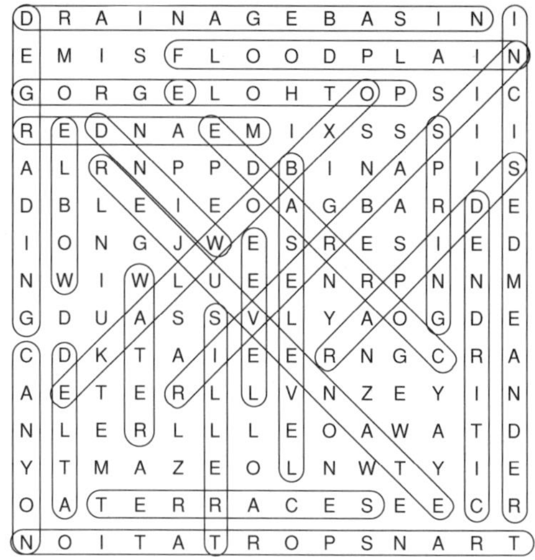

1 MISSISSIPPI, 2 NILE, 3 GANGES, 4 INDUS, 5 YANGTZE, 6 YELLOW, 7 AMAZON, 8 WYE

A46 - Coasts (2)

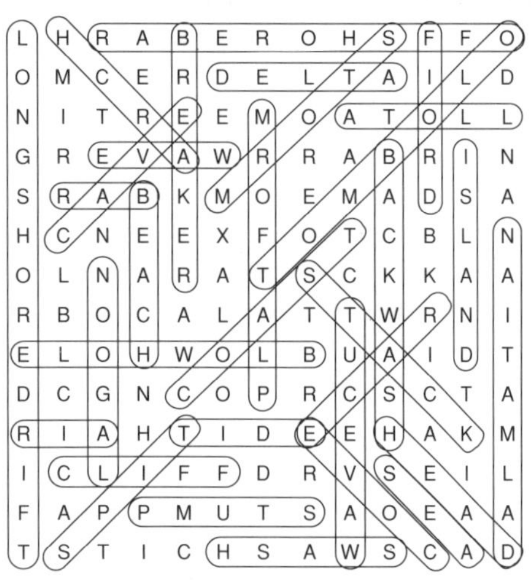

1 MEDITERRANEAN, 2 BLACK, 3 BALTIC, 4 NORTH, 5 ADRIATIC

A47 - Clouds and rain (2)

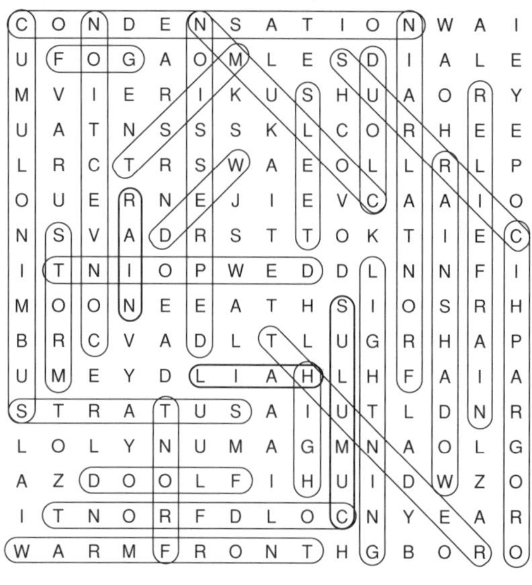

1 WAIALEALE, 2 VERKHOYANSK, 3 CHERRAPUNJI, 4 VOSTOK, 5 DEATH VALLEY, 6 DALLOL, 7 YUMA, 8 ALAZIZIYAH, 9 BO

A48 - Lakes

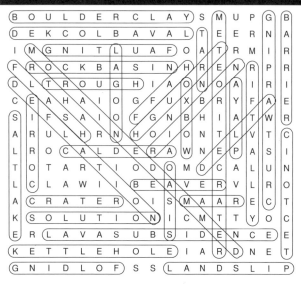

B O U L D E R C L A Y S M U P G B
D E K C O L B A V A L T E E R N A
I M G N I T L U A F O A T R M I R
F R O C K B A S I N H R E N R P R
D L T R O U G H I A O N O A I R I
C E A H A I O G F U X B R Y F A E
S I F S A I O F G N B H I A T W R
A R U L H R N H O I O N T L V T C
L R O C A L D E R A W N E P A S I
T O T A R T I O D O M D C A L U N
L C L A W I I B E A V E R V L R O
A C R A T E R O I S M A A R E C T
K S O L U T I O N I C M T T Y O C
E R L A V A S U B S I D E N C E E
K E T T L E H O L E I A R D N E T
G N I D L O F S S L A N D S L I P

1 SUPERIOR, 2 MICHIGAN, 3 HURON, 4 ONTARIO, 5 MALAWI, 6 VICTORIA, 7 NESS

A49 - Tropical areas

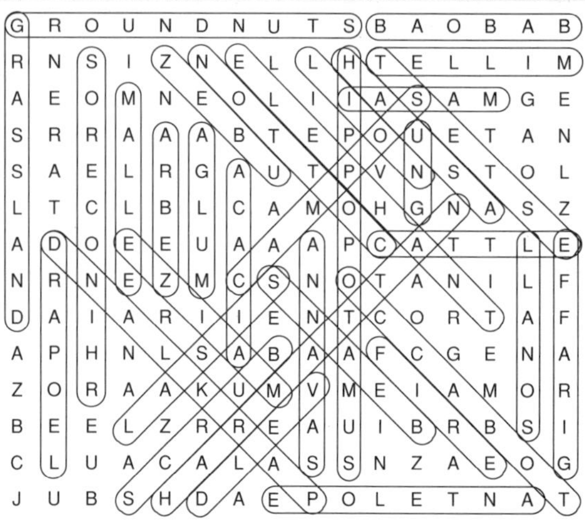

1 NILE, 2 NIGER, 3 TANA, 4 VOLTA, 5 ZAIRE, 6 ORANGE, 7 ZAMBEZI, 8 CUANZA, 9 JUBA

A50 - Mediterranean areas

R O S E M A R Y D O O W D E R
E R M I G W A L N U T S N N E
U H Y O R N E O C C O R I S D
C T R J A R R A H T I S S S N
A E T B P E A A R C I B M E A
L M L P E O E K L A O O A R E
Y P E B F I G S R M R R H P L
P E V E R G R E E N O A K Y O
T R S I U Q A M O Q C N A C C
U A R N I O T N I E U O D S H
S T L E T M V H D A L O O E A
R E D N O I T A G I R R I P P
L E M O N A R R V U A J U A A
L A R T S I M E C N O A R R R
G B G O R S E U G I R R A G R
T S A O C T S E W E D I D Z A
L E V E C H E R E D N E V A L

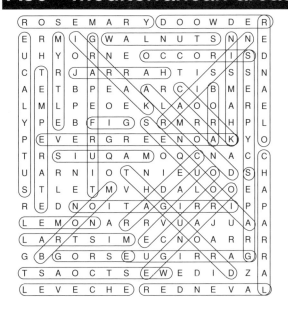

1 RHONE, 2 TIBER, 3 PO, 4 EBRO, 5 ARNO, 6 NILE,
7 VARDAR, 8 JUCAR, 9 GEDIZ

A51 - Middle latitudes

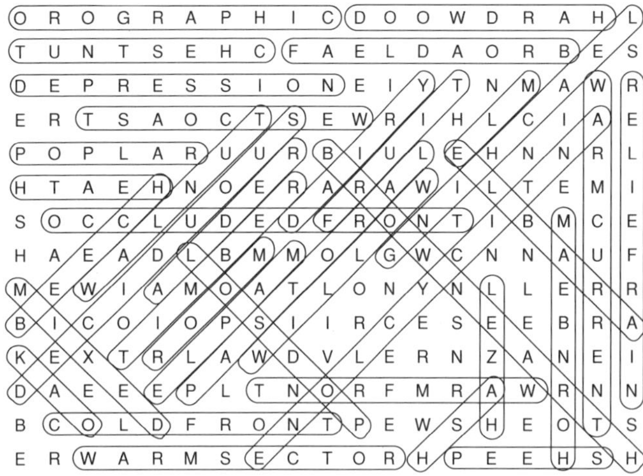

1 SEINE, 2 RHINE, 3 SHANNON, 4 LOIRE, 5 SEVERN, 6 ELBE,
7 WESER

A52 - Tropical forests

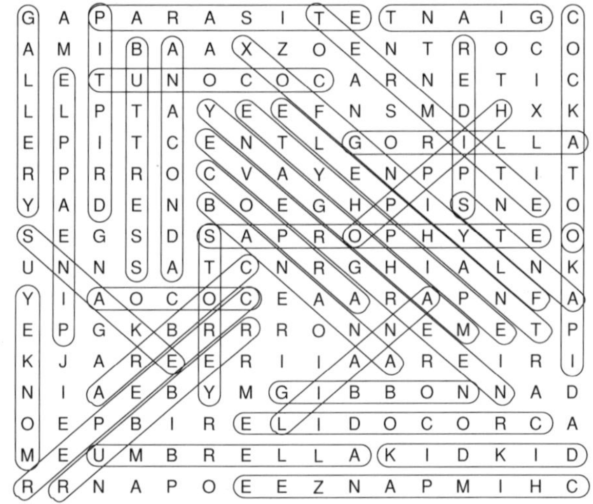

1 AMAZON, 2 TOCANTINS, 3 XINGU, 4 NEGRO, 5 JARI,
6 IRIRI, 7 MADEIRA, 8 NAPO

A53 - New towns (1)

1 Basildon 2 Bracknell 3 Stevenage 4 Livingston
5 Milton Keynes 6 Washington 7 Telford 8 Redditch
9 Llantrisant 10 Corby 11 Harlow 12 Crawley

A54 - New towns (2)

1 Hemel Hempstead 2 Welwyn Garden City 3 Skelmersdale
4 Peterlee 5 Glenrothes 6 East Kilbride 7 Cumbernauld
8 Warrington 9 Newton Aycliffe 10 Hatfield 11 Northampton
12 Peterborough

A55 - Islands quiz

1 Corsica 2 Crete 3 Sardinia 4 Malta 5 Cyprus
6 Lundy 7 Man 8 Skye 9 Rhodes 10 Guernsey
11 Ceylon/Sri Lanka 12 Galapagos or Aldabra 13 Canaries
14 Madeira 15 St. Helena 16 Tasmania 17 Bikini
18 Falklands 19 Midway 20 Easter Island 21 Pitcairn
22 Solomon 23 Ithaca 24 Fair Isle

A56 - Where on Earth ...? (1)

(A) France (B) Spain (C) Germany (D) Italy (E) UK
(F) India (G) China (H) Russia/CIS (I) Japan
(J) Australia (K) Canada (L) USA

A57 - Where on Earth ...? (2)

(A) Ghana (B) Nigeria (C) Egypt (D) Kenya
(E) South Africa (F) Israel (G) Saudi Arabia (H) Pakistan
(I) Bangladesh (J) Indonesia (K) New Zealand

A58 - Where on Earth ...? (3)

(A) Denmark (B) Netherlands (C) Belgium (D) Portugal
(E) Greece (F) Mexico (G) Venezuela (H) Peru
(I) Brazil (J) Argentina

A59 - British rivers (3)

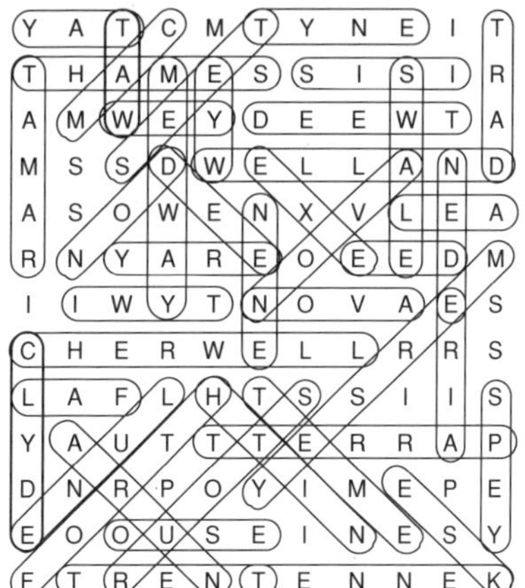

1 MISSISSIPPI

A60 - European countries (3)

```
S W I T Z E R L A N D S L E S S
P S U A O R E B D E N M A R K A
A I A S I C G R A D A V E H N I
I L R N E R A H B E L G I U M V
N F B E M Y A N P W N E A N A A
N A R A L A G G O S I R I G I L
O G E A N A R B L M F M R A N S
R E T R N I N I A U N A T R A O
W I M L O C A D N H B N S Y M G
A K C O T S E B D O U Y U C U U
Y U R P O R T U G A L E A S R Y
T I A I K A V O L S O H C E Z C
```

1 BRUSSELS, 2 S' GRAVENHAGE, 3 BERN, 4 STOCKHOLM, 5 BUCURESTI

A61 - Asian capitals

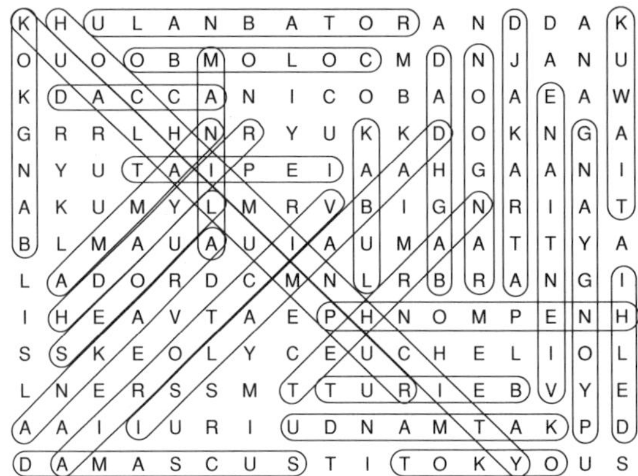

1 ANDAMAN, 2 NICOBAR, 3 RYUKYU, 4 KURIL, 5 MALDIVE, 6 SEYCHELLES, 7 MAURITIUS

A62 - Asian countries (3)

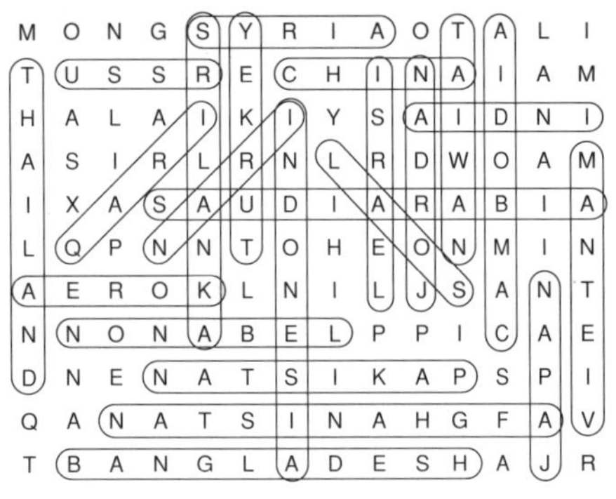

1 MONGOLIA, 2 MALAYSIA, 3 PHILIPPINES, 4 QATAR

A63 - American countries (2)

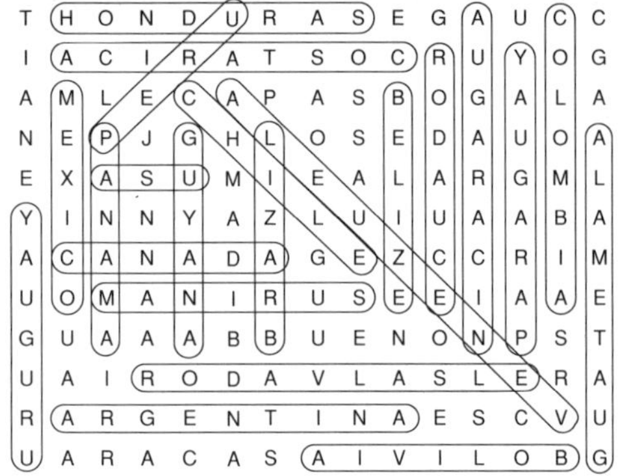

1 TEGUCIGALPA, 2 SAN JOSE, 3 MANAGUA, 4 BUENOS AIRES, 5 CARACAS

A64 - American capitals (2)

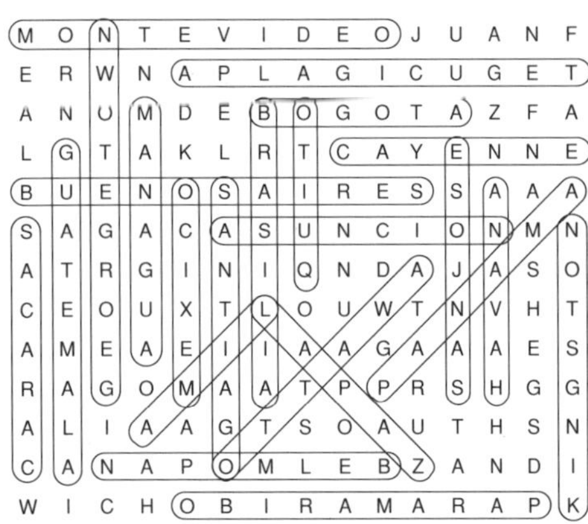

1 JUAN FERNANDEZ, 2 FALKLAND, 3 SOUTH GEORGIA, 4 SOUTH SANDWICH

A65 - States of the USA (2)

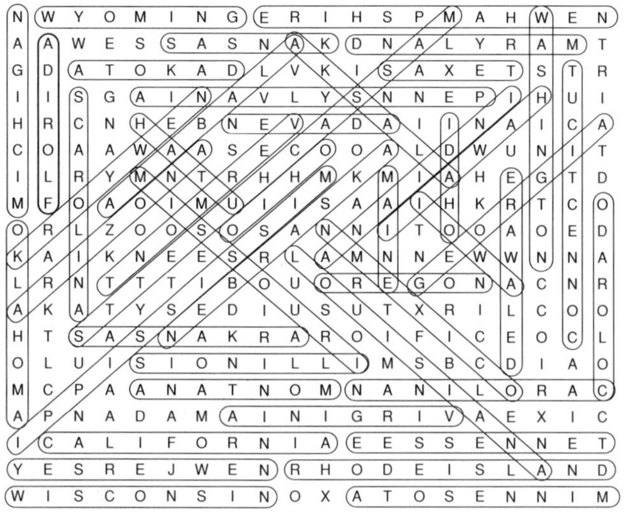

1 WEST VIRGINIA, 2 SOUTH DAKOTA, 3 KENTUCKY, 4 DISTRICT OF COLUMBIA,
5 CANADA, 6 MEXICO

A66 - Counties of England & Wales

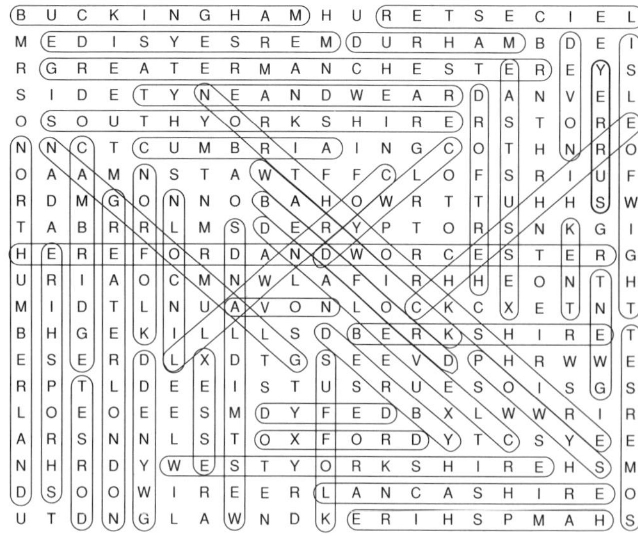

1 HUMBERSIDE, 2 NOTTINGHAM, 3 STAFFORD, 4 NORTHAMPTON,
5 GLOUCESTER, 6 WEST SUSSEX, 7 WILTSHIRE, 8 RUTLAND
FORMER COUNTY IS: HUMBERSIDE

A67 - Great lakes of the world (2)

A D R A G G R E A T B E A R
T N W T P T U R K A N A N P
H A I R O T C I V O E R I E
A G N N O N Y A N Y E G H T
B I N E P U L G R N R T M I
A H I A O G R E A T S A L T
S C P G E N A V S T L N B I
C I E H I T T T E A R A N C
A M G E N E V A W L P I H A
V L A K Y A B I R C A A A C
O S U P E R I O R I D R R A
L N O G I P I N A G O D A L
T A G U E V A L S T A E R G
A B O T I N A M H U R O N A

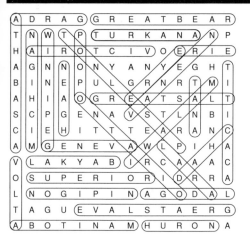

1 POYANG HU, 2 GREAT BITTER, 3 NICARAGUA

A68 - The weather station (2)

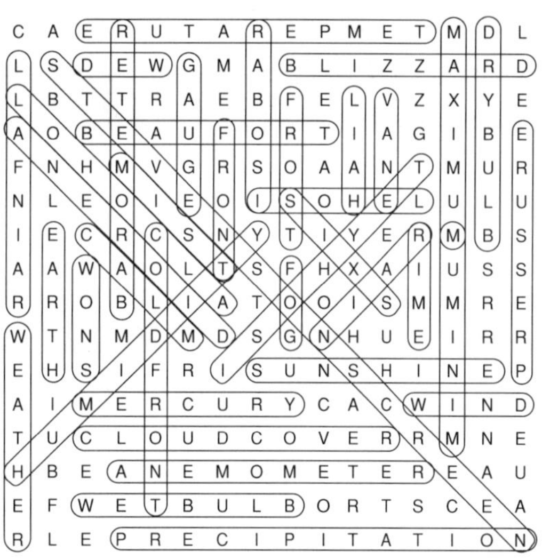

1 CALM, 2 BREEZE, 3 GALE, 4 STORM, 5 HURRICANE,
6 BEAUFORT SCALE

A69 - Energy

1 Transformer 2 Tanker 3 Thermal 4 Tides 5 Turbine 6 Fastbreeder 7 Fuel 8 Fusion 9 Fire 10 Fission 11 Geothermal 12 Gas 13 Generator 14 Grid 15 Greenhouse 16 Wave power 17 Well 18 Water mill 19 Wood 20 Windmill 21 Symbols 22 Steam 23 Shore oil 24 Solar 25 Sunshine

A70 - Settlements

1 Routes 2 Region 3 Museum 4 Mining 5 Models 6 Market 7 Office 8 Ghetto 9 Growth 10 Ribbon 11 Resort 12 Retail 13 Houses 14 Hamlet 15 Street 16 Square 17 Bridge 18 Blight 19 Exurbs 20 Social 21 Subway 22 Carrot 23 People 24 Public 25 Parcel 26 Shanty 27 School

A71 - Cops and robbers

1 Principal station 2 Main road 3 Cutting 4 Secondary road 5 Bridge 6 Gradient (1 in 5 or steeper) 7 Public convenience 8 Telephone 9 Milestone 10 Level crossing 11 Embankment 12 Wood 13 Orchard 14 Windmill 15 Television mast 16 Viewpoint 17 Quarry 18 Spoil heap 19 Forestry Commission wood 20 Triangulation pillar 21 Viaduct 22 Public house 23 Church with tower 24 Greenhouse 25 Footpath 26 Powerline (electricity transmission line) 27 Tunnel 28 Golf course 29 Railway station

A72 - Our town

1 Museum 2 Battlefield 3 Castle 4 Cathedral 5 Town Hall 6 Railway station 7 Bridge 8 Road 9 River 10 Motorway 11 Park 12 Place of tourist interest 13 Golf course 14 Bus station 15 Churches and chapels 16 Church with tower 17 Views 18 Triangulation pillar 19 Public houses 20 Public conveniences 21 Parking

A73 - A railway journey

1 Principal station 2 Cathedral 3 Town Hall 4 Tunnel 5 Embankment 6 Chimneys 7 Closed railway station 8 Cutting 9 Bridge 10 Viaduct 11 Church with spire 12 Woods 13 Orchards 14 Greenhouses 15 Bridges 16 Level crossings 17 Cemetery 18 Sidings 19 Railway station 20 Bus station

A74 - Our holiday

1 Caravan park 2 Camping site 3 Youth hotel 4 Woods 5 Stream/river 6 Railway line 7 Railway station 8 Bus station 9 Ancient monument 10 National Trust 11 Beach 12 Cliffs 13 Shingle 14 Rocks 15 Telephone 16 Coastguard 17 Lifeboat station 18 Heliport 19 Church with spire 20 Cathedral 21 Museum 22 Public house 23 Parking place 24 Toilet/public convenience 25 Motorway 26 Hospital 27 Bridge 28 Dual carriageway 29 Golf course 30 Clubhouse 31 Post office 32 Information Centre 33 Foothpaths 34 Park

A75 - Gran's place

1 Motorway 2 Junction 2 3 Service station 4 Junction 12 5 Motoring organisation telephone 6 Viaduct 7 Power line (electricity transmission line) 8 Secondary road 9 Steep hill/gradient 1:5 or more) 10 Bridge 11 Unfenced minor road 12 Wood 13 Triangulation pillar 14 Milestone 15 Post office 16 Chapel/small church 17 School 18 Quarry 19 Youth hostel 20 Footpath 21 Stream 22 Footbridge 23 Camping site 24 Parking 25 Radio/television mast